# 4.

# *'Waste Not, Want Not'*

# 'Waste Not, Want Not'

*Food preservation from
early times to the present day*

EDITED BY C. ANNE WILSON

Edinburgh University Press

Papers from the Fourth Leeds Symposium
on Food History and Traditions,
April 1989

Edinburgh University Press
22 George Square, Edinburgh

Typeset in Alphacomp Garamond
by Pioneer Associates Limited, Perthshire, and
printed in Great Britain by
Page Bros Ltd, Norwich


British Library Cataloguing
in Publication Data

Waste not, want not: Food preservation in Britain
from early times to the present day.
– (Food and society series)
I. Wilson, Anne C.      II. Series
664.009

ISBN 0 7486 0119 8 (cased)

# Contents

*About the contributors*

*List of illustrations*

**1.**
*Introduction*
1

**2.**
*Preserving Food to Preserve Life: the Response to
Glut and Famine from Early Times to the
End of the Middle Ages*
C. ANNE WILSON
5

**3.**
*Pots for Potting: English Pottery and its Role in
Food Preservation in the Post-mediaeval Period*
PETER BREARS
32

**4.**
*Necessities and Luxuries: Food Preservation from
the Elizabethan to the Georgian Era*
JENNIFER STEAD
66

**5.**
*Industrial Food Preservation in the
Nineteenth and Twentieth Centuries*
H. G. MULLER
104

**6.**
*Nineteenth- and Twentieth-Century Trends in
Food Preserving: Frugality, Nutrition or Luxury*
LYNETTE HUNTER
134

*Index*
159

# About the contributors

PETER BREARS is the Director of Leeds City Museum. He combines his interests in archaeology, architecture and the traditional food of Northern England with a great deal of practical experience of recreating the culinary confections of earlier centuries. His publications include *The Gentlewoman's Kitchen: Great Food in Yorkshire 1650-1750* and *Traditional Food in Yorkshire.*

LYNETTE HUNTER is a Senior Lecturer at the University of Leeds' Institute of Bibliography and Textual Criticism. She has published several books and articles on modern English literature, and is general editor of *Household and Cookery Books Published in Britain* 1800-1914.

H. G. MULLER was born in Germany and came to England in 1946. He spent the first twenty years of his working life in the food industry, and is now a Senior Lecturer in the Procter Department of Food Science at the University of Leeds, where he has been teaching students since 1964. His publications include *Nutrition and Food Processing* (with G. Tobin), *Baking and Bakeries*, and *An Introduction to Tropical Food Science.*

JENNIFER STEAD trained as an art historian and writes on social history and food history. Her publications include *Food and Cooking in 18th Century Britain.*

ANNE WILSON has worked for many years in the Brotherton Library of the University of Leeds, becoming involved in food history as a result of cataloguing the John Preston

*About the contributors*

Collection of early English cookery books. Her publications include *Food and Drink in Britain from the Stone Age to Recent Times* and *The Book of Marmalade*. She is currently researching the very early history of distilling.

# List of illustrations

1. Catching and smoking salmon, from Olaus Magnus, *Historiae de gentibus septentrionalibus*, 1555.
2. A keg of bog butter found at Kilmaluag, Skye, in 1931.
3. Pasties and pies.
4. Potting pots.
5. Salting pots.
6. Ham pans.
7. Butter pots.
8. Preserve and pickling jars.
9. Bread pots.
10. Salt packing of herrings in Lowestoft, *ca.* 1900.
11. A whole pickled pig exhibited at the Great Exhibition in London in 1851.
12  i. Drying coffee beans, *ca.* 1880.
   ii. Drying coffee beans, *ca.* 1960.
13. Smoking strips of moose in Canada, *ca.* 1880.
14. Cake of portable soup made in 1771.
15. Frozen mammoth found in the ice in Siberia in 1799.
16. Ice house near the old city wall in York.
17. A horse-drawn ice-marker.
18. Ice-machine designed by Jacob Perkins in 1834.
19. Frigidaire domestic refrigerator, 1939 model.
20. A modern butter packaging plant.
21. Appert as he appeared on a French postage stamp in 1955.
22. Appert's apparatus as it appears in his book.
23. A 4 lb can of roasted veal manufactured by Donkin and Gamble, 1824.
24. Three piece soldered tinplate can; and two piece drawn aluminium can.

## List of illustrations

25. Soldering tin canisters, *ca.* 1850.
26. Battery of retorts for can sterilisation.
27. The hydrostat steriliser.
28. Automatic pallet irradiation.

# 1.

## *Introduction*

Famine is still a grim reality in the Third World, and for many centuries it was a reality in this country too. The varied ways in which surplus food has been conserved in former times to make it available for the seasons of scarcity form the subject of our book.

Today we are not seriously affected if crops grown in the British Isles fail through drought or excessive rain, or if over-fishing leads to a dearth of fish from the seas around us. Any dearth of local foodstuffs can be overcome through trade with other countries in other climatic regions; and we pay for both necessary and luxury foods brought into our ports by exporting a wide range of goods and services, some of them, like computer-related skills, far removed from the realm of food production.

It is true that even in our affluent society there are still some people who suffer from malnutrition, usually linked with poverty and an unwillingness to live on a diet based on the cheapest foodstuffs because they tend to be boring, stodgy and untempting to the appetite. Yet today the poorest people are not likely to practise food preservation, buying cheaply at times of glut; for even gluts have a fairly small effect on shop prices when high labour and transport costs and high rents have to be built into the equation. Moreover, the poorest people often lack the equipment, storage vessels and space necessary for preserving food on a worthwhile scale. Today the favourite type of domestic food preservation is probably deep-freezing. This requires ownership of a freezer, a large garden to grow fruit and vegetables, and usually a car to cater for expeditions to country farms to pick strawberries and other soft fruit, and to buy quarters or more of sheep or pig carcasses. This kind of preserving is the province of the comfortably off middle classes.

The situation was very different in past centuries, and the phrase *Waste Not, Want Not*, chosen as the title for the Fourth Leeds Symposium on Food History and Traditions held in April 1989, reflects the theme which underlay most of the food-preserving efforts of our forebears. The papers read at the Symposium are the basis of the chapters of our book, and they follow the theme from the first beginnings to the present day.

Many of the methods of preservation in common use in the Middle Ages went back to very early times indeed, and chapter 2 on *Preserving Food to Preserve Life*, by Anne Wilson, illustrates the ways in which those methods were practised, and shows how some survived far beyond the Middle Ages in remoter parts of Britain and elsewhere in the world. The underlying principles still influence the preservation processes of today. Commercial bacon-curing reflects the salting and smoking of hams and bacon carried out by the Celts in pre-Roman times, and modern grain storage in silos relies on the same biochemical reaction as the underground pit storage practised in southern England in the Iron Age.

In chapter 3, *Pots for Potting: English Pottery and its Role in Food Preservation in the Post-mediaeval Period*, Peter Brears demonstrates the relationship between contents and the vessels used to contain them for a mode of food conservation that was highly popular before the advent of canning. A typology for the potting pots of different parts of England and Wales has never previously been compiled, and his illustrations for the chapter now supply one.

Chapter 4, entitled *Necessities and Luxuries: Food*

# Introduction

*Preservation from the Elizabethan to the Georgian Era*, by Jennifer Stead, comprises a wide-ranging survey of the principal ways in which food was preserved in the seventeenth and eighteenth centuries with especial emphasis on meat and fish. Most of the food conservation within that period was still being carried out on a small domestic scale, with animals slaughtered one at a time, and the carcass of each one divided up into parts to be salted, soused or otherwise treated to save them for later consumption. During the eighteenth century there emerged certain new or further developed preservation techniques suitable for exploitation on a much larger scale, and in our fifth chapter, *Industrial Food Preservation in the Nineteenth and Twentieth Centuries*, by H. G. Muller, some early factory processes of preservation are described. These have since been further refined and modernised in a variety of ways, and the twentieth century has seen the invention of new techniques such as freeze-drying and irradiation. Commercially preserved foodstuffs now supply a substantial part of the nation's diet.

Once the mass-preserved, factory-produced foods were available for sale in shops throughout the land, the need for carrying out preserving activities at home was much diminished, though such activities have never completely ceased. Our last chapter, *Nineteenth- and Twentieth-century Trends in Food Preserving: Frugality, Nutrition or Luxury*, by Lynette Hunter, takes the form of an enquiry into the ways in which the practice of home-preserving has been influenced and modified by the industrial revolution and the widespread availability of shop-bought preserved foodstuffs.

Today the freezing of fruit and vegetables and the making of jam and marmalade are probably the two kinds of preservation most often carried out at home. To some extent they link up with other present-day food trends, such as concern about the use of chemicals in growing and processing the factory-produced versions. Some of those

3

who blanch and freeze their own vegetables have chosen to grow them organically in the first place because so many of the vegetables on sale in shops, whether fresh or frozen, contain the residues of chemical fertilisers and pesticides. In past centuries heavily-salted foods were believed to induce scurvy, and worse, though many people were obliged to eat them in the absence of anything better.

The newest preserving technique is irradiation. Although scientists believe that lightly irradiated foods are perfectly safe to eat, it remains to be seen whether heavy consumption of them over a period of time can do some unforeseen damage to the consumer. But it is certain that in years to come irradiation will be overtaken by still newer methods of preservation which cannot even be guessed at as yet. In the meantime it is interesting to see what a long history some other contemporary preserving techniques have, and in our book we have presented the main aspects of food preservation in Britain from early times to the present day.

C. Anne Wilson,
Leeds
October 1990

# 2.

## Preserving Food to Preserve Life: The Response to Glut and Famine from Early Times to the End of the Middle Ages

### C. ANNE WILSON

In the past, the advances of civilisation have been closely linked with the alternation of food gluts and food famines. Famines have always been unpredictable since they result from vagaries of the climate, but they have provided the imperative for the development of methods whereby surplus food could be preserved in the years of glut. The cumulation of preserved foodstuffs over a series of good seasons eventually led to trade and barter, and the acquisition by the group offering the foods of new material objects and new ideas from people at a distance. One thinks of the Gauls sending their salted hams to Rome, and of the early Britons exporting their surplus corn to feed Roman soldiers in mainland Europe, and of the Celtic princes in their turn receiving the coveted Mediterranean wines, and the wine-cups and other trappings of Roman civilisation.

Today salted pork in the form of ham or bacon seems to us to be one of the most typical of preserved foodstuffs, and one which has played an important part in the diet of Northern Europe throughout the historic period. But both meat and fish were being conserved long before the discovery of salt as an agent for preservation, and it is interesting to examine the methods by which primitive peoples met the challenges of food conservation before the use of salt was known. Not a great deal of evidence survives from very early prehistoric times, but the continuation of very simple conservation techniques into the twentieth century in other parts of the world helps us to realise that they were probably once carried out in Britain too. Their successful completion depends today upon climatic conditions, and must always have done so. The British climate underwent changes during the earlier prehistoric ages, and there were certainly periods when the primitive methods of preservation described below could have been practised. Some survived until a late date on a few Scottish islands.

**Drying:**
**flesh foods**
The simplest of all methods of preserving flesh foods is by air-drying. The early Egyptians were able to dry meat by air and sun alone in the arid climate of their country. Quite different climatic conditions, the cold, dry spring air of northern Norway with plenty of sun and plenty of wind, made it possible for the Norwegian fishermen of medieval times to preserve their catches of cod simply by air-drying the fish until it turned into the exceedingly hard stockfish, which was almost indestructible. Further west and south on the Faroe Islands, fish was still being hung up to dry out-of-doors in the late 1940s. Kenneth Williamson wrote in 1948 of fish hanging outside against the walls of the dwelling-house or the storage-house 'for a month or more, and when required [it] is taken down, skinned and cleaned, and boiled. Some hardy individuals do not trouble to boil it, but merely remove the skin and chew the fish just as it is, with obvious relish. It is a great stand-by when fresh fish is difficult to obtain'.[1] It was also regarded as a rather special delicacy to be served to visitors, and was a part of the fare for Christmas.

Another air-dried foodstuff of the Faroese was whalemeat, which they cut into strips and hung up out-of-doors. Williamson found the flavour of both dried fish and whalemeat quite intolerable, but the native Faroese who had been familiar with them from childhood evidently had no difficulty in acquiring the taste for them. This method of preservation is the most primitive of all, and we can safely deduce that it was in common use among the inhabitants of parts of mainland north-western Europe from the earliest times, and that they would not have been deterred at all by the high and strange flavours of meat and fish cured in this manner.

Successful air-drying out of doors is very dependent on climatic conditions. Williamson explained that the dried fish 'develops best in fine dry weather, and is liable to spoil if the weather is wet'. The hunters and fishermen of very early times probably learned to erect at least a sheltering roof supported on timber poles over their fleshfoods as they dried in the air.[2] Much later more substantial drying-houses of stone were still in use on some islands off north-west Scotland. The people on St Kilda built theirs in the form of stone pyramids, with the stones arranged so as to allow gaps for the passage of air; and Martin Martin who visited the island in 1698 reported that the inhabitants ate fatty sea-fowls, such as the fulmar and the solan goose or gannet, 'being dried in their storehouses, without any salt or spice to preserve them'. The solan geese were kept 'for the space of a whole year' in this manner, and were then either boiled or roasted and eaten.[3] Martin explained elsewhere that on the island of Skye newly-caught herrings were gutted and hung up to dry in pairs on a rope stretched across the house, adding that the herrings thus dried 'eat well and free from putrefaction after eight months keeping in this fashion'.[4] Today at the Corrigall farm museum on Orkney, a typical small stone-built farmhouse furnished in the style of the 1860s, one can see herrings strung up near (but not too near) the fire in the 'in-by' which was the family living-room.

Jorgen Landt served as a clergyman on the Faroe Islands from 1791–1798 and wrote an account of the islanders which was subsequently translated into English. He described their purpose-built structures for the drying of meat and fish, made from timber laths nailed to corner-posts with half-inch gaps between them to give a free passage to the wind, and roofed with straw and grass-turf.[5] More substantial storehouses for fish, with a stone wall at either end and side-walls of laths, were erected near the sea-shore.

The Faroese were still maintaining their drying-houses in the 1940s, and it is interesting to compare the accounts by Landt and by Williamson of how one particular delicacy, a young lamb, was prepared there. The carcase was skinned and gutted, and then cut open and spread out flat, and in that form was hung up and left to dry for a few months.[6] Both writers explain that this was, traditionally, a food to be offered as a treat to special guests. In the 1940s it was usually boiled and served with potatoes.

Pieces of mutton were left in the drying-house exposed to air-currents for several months longer, during which the flesh underwent further changes. At the end of that time, according to Williamson, 'It has a strong flavour and a stronger smell, is the dark red colour of congealed blood, and is like toffee to chew. Its taste is an acquired one which most Britons at once decide they can very well do without; but having persevered, I am inclined to agree with Faroe folk that nothing more tasty or sustaining is to be found in the islands.' The cured mutton was sliced into thin slivers and eaten raw; 'and the fatter it is, the nearer it approaches perfection'.[7]

The curing of the meat and its subsequent 'high' flavour are brought about by chemical changes in its composition over a long period of time. It might be expected that the outer parts of the raw flesh would be particularly vulnerable to attack by flies and airborne microbes during the early stages of the drying process, but Williamson was surprised how little of the wind-dried meat and fish on the Faroes became maggoty, considering the abundance of blue-bottles there in the summer months. If most of the surface grows dry and hard quite quickly through exposure to sun and wind, then only the moist part at the bottom where the body-fluids cumulate will be prone to attack by insects and microbes; and even then the results may be washed out as the fluids drip down and drain away.

Wind-drying is practised today in various parts of the world. Ducks are wind-dried in China. Biltong is prepared in a number of countries where the climate is sufficiently warm and dry. To make it, the flesh of cattle, sheep, goats or camels, is cut lengthwise along the fibres into strips, and hung up on wires. Nowadays, however, the meat is salted first, which helps to extrude the body-liquids more quickly, thus speeding up the process. Britain had a much sunnier and drier climate during the late Neolithic period and the Bronze Age than it has today, so both meat and fish could have been dried successfully then, even without salt.

Another very primitive method of preservation is by burial. This has long been a custom in the Scandinavian countries, where the earliest written record connected with the underground storage of fish goes back to the fourteenth century, though the practice must have begun much earlier than that. Sharks' flesh and other fish are still preserved by a similar process in Iceland.[8] In the 1940s, the Faroe islanders buried cods' heads in the earth (or kept them in a box or tin) until they became very high, when they were resurrected, washed and scraped clean, had their gills removed, and after a quarter of an hour's boiling were ready to bring to table.[9]

*Burial: flesh foods and dairy products*

The initial discovery of the advantages of burial must go back to the prehistoric period, and most probably to the time when men lived by hunting and fishing, and did not want to waste part of the catch when a really successful foray brought in more than they and their families could eat while it remained fresh. Deep burial in the earth saved the meat or fish from predators, and kept it cool enough to prevent the growth either of moulds or of the microbes that cause botulism. Air-borne infections could not reach it, and it slowly fermented with its own yeasts and enzymes. As this happened, the flesh softened – an advantage in the case of the sinewy game animals. The final flavour was strong and high.

The idea that venison should be buried in the ground for a short period to get rid of 'reesting' recurs in the cookery books of the late Middle Ages.[10] 'Reesting' meant the evil-smelling rancidity of meat beginning to go bad. Venison had a peculiar position in the dietary of the period. It could not be bought or sold legally. Deer could be hunted only by the king and his huntsmen, and by the great lords who held their hunting-forests in fealty to the king. But deer were often poached, either by lowlier folk, or by members of other noble families who kept up their family feuds by this means. Once killed, the deer either had to be removed from the forest very quickly, or else rapidly hidden to be recovered later. 'Reesting' could well have been a genuine problem when the recovery of the carcass was delayed, but it could also have been a problem even when the venison was legitimately hunted, dismembered by the gamekeeper (who received his own small share of the meat), and taken straight home by its rightful owner – it could not always be cooked warm from the kill, and if it was hung overlong in larder or other outbuilding, then 'reesting' might again be the result.

Yet the medieval recipe calls for burial of the venison in the earth for three days to do away with 'reestiness' [rancidness] at a period when the obvious treatment for such a development would have been by washing the meat with solutions of brine or vinegar reinforced with pepper or ginger. My suggestion is that an earlier tradition underlies the recipe whereby venison was formerly buried in the ground to discourage infestation by insects during the time it took for it to become tender enough to eat. In still earlier times the meat could have been left for a good deal longer than that, for the hunting communities of the pre-farming era would not have wished to lose any part of a

**1.**
A keg of bog butter
found at Kilmaluag,
Skye, in 1931.

big catch of deer or wild cattle or pigs. Unfortunately, such a practice does not leave the same sort of mark in the archaeological record as a hoard of coins does; so there is very little proof of a form of preservation that is likely to have been customary in the remote past.

Another buried foodstuff has left very definite traces. 'Bog butter' has been discovered at a number of places in Scotland and Ireland, usually buried in peat. It has been described as 'one of the commonest finds in Irish bogs'.[11] The custom of burying kegs of butter continued in Ireland until late in the eighteenth century, if not later, and records of the time said that it took seven years to produce the desired flavour. The peat supplied a cool storage place while the butter matured. In practice, this meant that it achieved a certain amount of lactic fermentation, coupled with the production of butyric acid, and thereafter ceased to change further and remained stable. Some bog butter was found during peat-cutting on the island of Skye in 1931 in a very water-logged condition. After it had been dried out, Professor J. Ritchie tried a little of it, and found it tasted like rancid butter, with a slight acrid flavour and a long, acidic aftertaste.[12] The burial of the butter may well have been partly linked with the desire to provide against famine in a time of glut, but it does also seem to reflect the positive wish to turn the butter into what was regarded as a delicacy by changing its flavour.

According to Lucas Debes' *Description of the Feroes, 1670* (translated into English in 1676), the Faroe islanders melted down sheep's tallow, cast it in large pieces, and buried them in moist earth 'to keep it, it growing the better the longer it is kept, and when it is old and is cut, it tasteth like old cheese'.[13] This type of preserving pays a double dividend, since the product is accessible throughout its period of storage as a defence against famine, and is finally brought out and eaten as a delicacy.

A further refinement on earth burial as a method of preservation was the deliberate use of ashes instead of simple earth. Sir Lindsay Scott made a survey of all the recorded examples in the British Isles of the underground chambers of late Iron Age and Roman date, known as souterrains. They occur in Cornwall, Ireland, Scotland and some northern islands, attached variously to round houses, hut circles, raths, forts and northern brochs, and they have been found in greater frequency on the more northerly sites. Within the souterrains, which Scott interpreted as underground storage-chambers, were discovered animal bones, a certain amount of grain, both loose and within storage-jars, and very often quantities of charcoal and wood-ash. He believed that the ash had been placed there deliberately for storage purposes, and he cited the practice of using ash to preserve the eggs of sea-fowl inside the stone-pyramid storehouses on the Isle of St Kilda, as described by Martin Martin after his visit there in 1695:

> They preserve their eggs in their stone-pyramids,
> scattering the burnt ashes of turf under and about
> them to defend them from the air, dryness being
> their only preservative and moisture their
> corruption; they preserve them six, seven or eight

12

months, as above said; and then they become
appetising and loosening, especially those that begin
to turn.[14]

The presence of animal bones in the underground
chambers surveyed by Scott suggests that fleshmeat may
have been stored there, and even, in those chambers which
had apertures to admit air, dried there. The possibility that
joints of meat were packed around with ashes and left to
mature cannot be ruled out. Martin reported that sea-fowls
were cured in the ashes of seaweed within cows' hides on a
small island off South Uist, 'which preserves them from
putrefaction'.[15]

A burial technique was also used to conserve seedcorn in
pre-Roman Britain and in other parts of northern Europe
during the same period. Archaeologists have made this
deduction after carrying out experimental work with a
view to discovering the purpose of the many beehive-
shaped pits found on Iron Age settlement sites in southern
England. When grain is packed into similar pits today and
the upper surface is sealed with an airtight seal, the
respiratory cycle of the grain gradually exhausts the oxygen
within the pit, replacing it with carbon dioxide. The outer
'skin' of grain lying next to the walls of the pit in fact
begins to sprout but eventually dies through lack of oxygen.
By then enough air has been removed from within the pit
for the rest of the grain to become dormant; the low
temperature through winter inhibits the growth of
microbes and fungi, and most (approximately 90 per cent
of the seedcorn thus stored will germinate and grow next
season. Interestingly, the same principle of replacing
oxygen with carbon dioxide makes possible the storage of
grain in silos today.

The Iron Age pits lay open through the summer, and in
the early autumn they were cleaned out, probably by using
hands and hand-tools, and then sterilised with an intense
flame fire. Where a few last cereal grains from the previous

**Burial: cereals**

harvest were still lying about on the floor of the pit they took the flame: hence the occasional finds of carbonised grains when the later infill of such pits is removed by archaeologists. If the pits were maintained in this fashion they could have been used and re-used over many seasons, and the cereals stored in them each year would have remained in good condition, provided the weather was not abnormally wet. Failure occurred only when the very heavy winter rainfall made the surrounding earth boggy and flooded into the pits below ground level. The quantities of grain contained by the pits were very large, and this method of storage is considered to have been suitable only for that part of the harvest destined for use as seedcorn for the next season.[16]

**Parching**  Parching was another technique employed to help preserve grain, specifically the grain required for future use as breadcorn. Pit storage would not have proved satisfactory for the cereals needed for daily food because frequent opening of the pits during the winter months, and the gradual removal of more and more of the contents, would have allowed air to penetrate and disturb the carbon dioxide built up within. Large storage jars standing above ground were probably the solution even in the earlier Iron Age, and in the time of the Belgae, the sophisticated Celtic tribe who inhabited south-east England during the last century before the Roman occupation, pit storage was going out of fashion altogether.

The parching of the grain was necessary not only to prevent sprouting while it was in the storage jars, but also to prevent rotting, for it often had to be harvested wet in the damp Iron Age climate. The parching may have been carried out by spreading the grain over clay constructions of a slightly domed shape which could be heated by fire from below.[17] In Roman Britain spelt (a soft wheat) was an important crop, and it particularly needed to be parched before it was stored for winter breadmaking. Under Roman

14

influence, corn-drying areas came into use with flues to convey the heat from a fire built in a trench below ground level. In the third and fourth centuries A.D. these had been developed into carefully insulated structures with double floors and underground flues, and their use became widespread. Corn-drying kilns were part of the equipment of Anglo-Saxon farms, too.[18]

There is evidence at an early date for another, completely **Smoking** different method of conservation, also dependent on fire: the use of smoke as a preservative for flesh foods. We do not know when the technique of smoking was first discovered, presumably by people who were trying to speed up the drying process by hanging their meat or fish within reach of the heat of the fire, but not so close that it cooked. Here and there archaeologists have found fairly substantial evidence for large-scale smoking at a very early date. About

**2.**
Catching and smoking salmon, from Olaus Magnus, *Historiae de gentibus septentrionalibus*, 1555.

the beginning of the second millenium B.C., a group of people were visiting a site close to the River Bann in Ireland, where they did some flint-working, probably to make points for fish-spears, and used many hearths which were covered by successive layers of ash, yet they did not leave any of the usual domestic debris of an ordinary settlement. The site has been interpreted as a summer fishing-camp beside the river, used by fishermen who built a weir on the river in order to catch salmon, and then dried and smoked the fish over the hearths.[19]

Smoke does not merely help to dry flesh foods; it also introduces formaldehyde which acts as a preservative, and it creates new interesting flavours to make the meat or fish more appetising. It was probably this enhancement of flavour which first encouraged people to experiment with the smoking of cheese. Columella commended the flavour of a Roman cheese which was first hardened in brine, and then smoked either with burning apple-tree wood or with the smoke from burning stubble.[20]

**Salting**   A tremendous advance took place in food preservation when free salt became available in reasonably large quantities. Salt was mined in Europe, in the eastern Alps, perhaps as early as the second millenium B.C., and knowledge of the techniques of salt-mining, and of the extraction of salt from brine springs, travelled slowly westwards. The Celts of the Iron Age, who reached Britain some time after 1,000 B.C., were the first people to practise salt-winning in this country. Their raw material was sea-water, and the remains of their salt-workings have been found at several places on the east and south coasts. In Lincolnshire the brine was evaporated in shallow earthenware dishes set on brick stands over gentle fires. In Norfolk, Essex and Kent, the sea-water was poured over clay bars, which were then heated to evaporate the water and leave the salt crystals to be scraped off.[21] During the Roman period, salt was still produced by the evaporation of sea-water in earthenware vessels, and supplies were augmented by salt produced at the brine springs of Droitwich and a place in Cheshire, possibly Middlewich: both places were called *Salinae* (meaning salterns). Salt evaporated on the beaches of Gaul was probably imported too.

Salt speeded up the drying process for flesh foods, drawing out the body fluids by osmosis, and giving some protection against microbial infection. After salting, fleshmeat could either be further dried, and perhaps smoked, or it could be preserved wet in fresh brine in jars or wooden barrels, and kept thus until needed. Thorough soaking was then required to get rid of excessive saltiness, and the meat could be cooked, preferably in a broth with vegetables or cereals to take up some of the remaining salt.

Roman authors reported how the succulent hams made by the Celts in Gaul and North Italy, and the salted mackerel and tuna prepared in Spain, were exported to other parts of the Empire, but they made no mention of British salted foods. But one of the Latin writing tablets found at Vindolanda contains a food list on which appears ham (*perna*), roe deer (*capraea*) red deer (*cervus*) and salt (*sal*), which could indicate that venison was already being salted, as well as pork.[22]

Milk and milk products entered the British diet when the first neolithic farmers brought their domesticated cows, sheep and goats into the country. Sour milk was the simplest milk product, which developed quickly when milk was kept in skin bags or coarse pottery vessels that could not be cleaned very thoroughly.[23] Sour milk becomes semi-solid, and when broken forms curds and whey. The curds, pressed together, drained and dried, formed a primitive curd cheese which could be kept for a short time.

**Preserving milk and cream**

Proper cheese-making began with the discovery of rennet. Rennet is the digestive juice secreted in the stomach-bag or vell of several mammals, and it is likely that when milk-curds were found inside the stomachs of young milk-fed calves, lambs and pigs slaughtered for meat, people not only ate the curds, but also had the idea of using the stomach-juice or even part of the stomach-lining to curdle other milk. They thus obtained a firmer curd and one that could be kept for a longer time than curds from milk soured only by the air and its bacteria. This was because rennet contains enzymes that continue to work within the curd over a long period, during which it begins to ripen into a hard cheese.[24] Certain plant juices have a similar, though weaker effect; and the use of plant juices in cheese-making was recorded by Columella, though the practice must go back long before the days of the Roman Empire.[25] Curds were drained through woven baskets or mats, and in Roman times by means of perforated pottery cheese-wrings, and they were then shaped into cheeses. Salt, once it became available, was added both to enhance flavour and to help draw out further moisture. After that, the cheeses were left to dry out slowly.

As a preserved foodstuff, cheese has great advantages, being very sustaining and also very portable, ideal for people who have to work or travel far from home, and a convenient product for marketing since it can be sent over long distances.

When the earliest farmers carried creamy milk about in skin bags, shaking it as they went along, they must have discovered that the cream was liable to separate itself from the rest of the liquid, forming itself into greasy lumps. At this point they had invented butter. It was a form of food that could be kept for some time, though in the prehistoric era, because of the organic residues which clung to the skin bags and unglazed pottery containers, it must nearly always have been consumed in a rancid state.

The production of butter by the shaking method continued late in parts of Scotland and the northern islands, as did the use of containers made of skin and the traditional pottery crogan to hold the milk or cream. Making butter in small quantities in this way could even become part of a social event. A description of butter-making in Melness in Sutherland about 1870, transmitted in Gaelic and then translated, ran as follows: 'They put the cream in the skin of a lamb or the skin of a sheep and they threw it from one to the other . . . By the time it had gone fourteen or fifteen times round the company, you had the butter.'[26]

In a very interesting survey published recently, J. Myrdal has tried to establish where and when the use of the plunge-churn first superseded the ancient shaking method of butter-making.[27] He identified the period as the eighth century A.D., and the place as the north-west corner of mainland Europe where examples of the perforated discs which used to be attached to the staffs of plunge-churns have been found on contemporary archaeological sites on South Jutland. The inspiration for the change in technique may have come from Asia, from the area where koumiss was produced by the fermentation of mares' milk. When Herodotus wrote in the fifth century B.C. about the preparation of koumiss among the Scythians, it was still being made by the shaking method.[28] At some later time it was discovered that fermentation could be speeded up by adding older sour milk to the new. It was probably at that point that a stick was introduced to mix the old and new milks together thoroughly. Then the idea of using a staff for an operation on milk formerly carried out by shaking the vessel somehow travelled west and linked itself to butter-making, and thus led to the invention of the plunge-churn, where the milk is agitated by the up-and-down motion of the staff. Thereafter the plunge-churn came into use in areas of large-scale butter production – in fact, the use of the churn may have tended to encourage the production of greater amounts of butter, while the old shaking method lingered on around the fringes, where only a little butter was prepared at a time.

As Europe settled down after the huge migrations of northern peoples that followed the collapse of the Roman Empire, the medieval cuisine began to emerge. The years of glut and the years of famine still had an enormous influence on diet. A great deal of food was preserved in various ways to make it available for the lean seasons, and so that it could be transported and traded more easily. Whereas the evidence for preserved foods in prehistoric and Roman Britain is rather scanty, the records from the Middle Ages allow us to trace not only when and how

**Salted meat and dairy products in the Middle Ages**

preserved foodstuffs were made and consumed, but also by whom they were eaten. The families of great lords made very different use of preserved foods from the families of peasants.

Animal foods were now nearly always preserved by wet-salting or dry-salting with or without the addition of smoking. The demand for salt was great, and constantly increasing. It was still obtained by the boiling down of seawater at many places around the coasts, and by the boiling of brine at the inland brine-springs; but all this salt was not enough, and Britain's salt was less suitable for curing flesh-meat and fish than the large-grained salt evaporated out by the sun alone on the beaches of Western France and Northern Spain and Portugal, known generally as Bay salt. That salt could penetrate flesh more thoroughly than the finer salt made by boiling, which tended to seal the surface tissues without entering further. It became a regular import and, in most households where salting was carried out, both kinds were purchased: Bay salt for preserving, and the finer white salt for the table. During the fourteenth century, saltpetre began to be used as a reinforcement to Bay salt in the curing of meat.[29]

Salting followed certain seasonal patterns. In the autumn some of the farm stock was killed off and salted to save winter feeding, though not to the extent that was once believed, for the household records of larger manors often show that the stock was slaughtered gradually week by week until Lent, so usually there would have been fresh meat on the table, as well as some salted meat. Autumn was the time when the peasant killed one or two of his pigs and salted them, perhaps selling the hams of one to pay for the salt. The rest was hung in the rafters and kept there to supply his family with a little bacon for their pottages until Lent and again at Easter. Well before Christmas in the manorial household, one or more boars from the forest, or boar-pigs from the domestic herd, were killed, and the head and shoulders put into a pickle of brine or brine and vinegar to make brawn for the festive season. Other parts of the animals were similarly pickled or soused, and served up as 'souse' to the servants and lesser folk.

In high summer, fresh beef and mutton were salted for a short time in a light brine, to prevent deterioration over the few days required for the consumption of the meat. Some farmers were prepared to salt down the meat of diseased animals which had died naturally, and to feed it to their labourers; but this practice was not generally approved.[30]

Salt venison was a valued addition to the diet of the households of royalty and of great men. Clarendon Place near Salisbury, which was a royal hunting lodge from the time of the Conquest to the end of the Middle Ages, contained a special salting-room or salsary, and several records survive of deer caught by the royal huntsmen in the nearby forest, salted and stored there, and eventually sent to Westminster or wherever else the king was keeping his Court.[31] A fourteenth-century recipe explains the contemporary method employed: the deer were dismembered and the pieces of meat soaked half a day in fresh water; they were dried, boiled in brine and left in it for three days and nights; then they were barrelled up, well-salted with new salt.[32] The household accounts of Richard de Swinburne, Bishop of Hereford, show how the venison was incorporated into the seasonal calendar. In November, the carcasses of the newly-slain deer were brought in to be salted; in the following May and June, salt venison made several appearances on the day by day menus.[33]

Early summer was the leanest time of year, before the young farm animals had fattened themselves on the new grass, or the cereal crops had ripened. The gentry might enjoy doves from their dovecotes, chickens from the poultry-yard and salted venison. But the peasant's bacon had all been used up and the breadcorn was running out, so that his family were reduced to eating bread made with beans, bran and oats, instead of the maslin or mixed wheat and rye available to them in times of plenty. That was the picture painted in Langland's poem, *Piers Plowman*.[34]

On the credit side, Piers Plowman had green [new] cheeses, curds and cream from his cow with her young calf, and leeks and spring onions for pottages to tide his family over to the harvest. Milk, curds and cheese, often referred to as 'white meats', were important in the diet of peasant labourers. Butter tended to be produced in the manorial dairy with the help of the churn, and seems more often to be associated with the diet and cookery of the well-to-do in lowland Britain. Where butter was made on a large scale on manors in the 'butter counties' of Suffolk and Essex, it was very heavily salted for long keeping and for marketing. When it was time to use the butter, most of the salt was washed out; and if it was intended for cooking purposes, the butter was melted and strained to clarify it.[35]

Butter itself came to have a special preservative function in one particular medieval confection: the cold pie. The contents of such pies often comprised highly-regarded fish, well-seasoned and baked. When the pie was cooked, the liquid within was poured out and the pie was filled up with melted, clarified butter which cooled to form an airtight seal around the fish. Pies thus sealed could be sent long distances, at least in winter, and there are several records of fish being despatched 'in bread', which was the medieval phrase used for fish sealed in pastry. Lampreys, rich river-fish much beloved by connoisseurs among royalty and the nobility (especially the Severn lampreys) were baked in pies and sent as presents. Rents were paid in pies of herrings or of eels. King Edward I, according to his wardrobe accounts, had luce from the stewponds of his estate at Langley in Essex sent to him in London 'in bread'.[36]

In the highland zone, where farming kept its strong pastoral element, the cows and sheep were taken up to the high pastures in the summer, and there both butter and cheese were made, the butter by the old shaking method.

Again, salt was a valued addition to both butter and cheese in the making, and there is some evidence that back at the homestead the cheeses were stored in a wet brine pickle until the time came to eat them.

Methods of cheese-making had changed little. In the lowland region, the hardest cheeses came from the butter-making counties, being produced there from skimmed milk. Hard cheese was fed to the peasants who did boon work on the manorial estates, to other labourers carrying out heavy manual tasks there, and to soldiers. The well-to-do rarely ate it, except perhaps in very small quantities at the end of a large meal, when they believed it helped to 'close' the stomach. They preferred cheese tarts made with softer and creamier cheeses already given the name of 'Brie', presumably because they resembled the cheese from that part of France.

## Salted fish in the Middle Ages

The other protein food preserved by salting, and in some cases also by smoking, was fish. The salting of fish was carried out either on board ship, or at the harbour as soon as the catch was landed. The so-called 'greenfish' were in fact white fish of various kinds, gutted and salted in barrels at sea when they were caught. 'Saltfish' were also white fish, which were salted immediately and then slowly dried on board the fishing vessel, when the fishermen were sailing in more northerly waters and the climate permitted drying.[37]

The herring fishery began early in the Middle Ages and at first the fish were salted whole in a very primitive fashion, but in the fourteenth century, the Dutch developed a technique, copied by the British, whereby the herring were gutted and then soaked for many hours in brine before being barrelled up in tight layers with salt between, thus keeping out the air which caused their fat to oxidise. These were known as white herrings.

Red herrings, alias 'baconned herrings', were made by a smoking technique developed in the late thirteenth century.

After prolonged soaking in strong brine, the fish were strung up in special smoking-houses and smoked for many hours. Then they too were stored in barrels. Vast quantities of both white and red herrings were prepared during the long summer season, and were sold at the ports and the great fairs for winter fast days and for the following Lent. They were some of the cheapest fish, consumed mainly by the poor. The well-to-do might eat them for breakfast (as did the Earl of Northumberland and his family when staying at their inland Yorkshire castles: the parents ate either red or white herrings, but the children were allowed only the more digestible white ones);[38] but herrings rarely appear on the menus or in the cookery books as a dish for the feasts of the nobility. When they do make a rare appearance along with various other kinds of fish for the first course of a fish-day meal, the entry reads: 'Baconned herring with sugar'.[39] It is a reminder that red herrings then were much more heavily smoked than the lightly 'kippered' herrings of recent times; so the sugar was no doubt introduced to abate the strong flavour of the smoking, just as it was used to abate the strong flavour of the vinegar in sweet-sour sauces.

Most of the dishes served on fish-days to the families of the nobility and greater gentry were in fact made from fresh seafish, shell-fish, or freshwater fish often taken from the ponds on their estates. A fisherman was among the retainers of the household, and he was sent to catch the fish conserved alive in the ponds when they were required.[40] For a large feast, however, a very varied assembly of fish dishes had to be produced in order to make up two or three abundant courses without any hint of repetition, so salted lamprey, salted salmon, salted eels and simple 'saltfish' took their place on menus side by side with the many varieties of fresh fish. The freshwater fish were valued more highly than even fresh seafish (as appears from those household accounts where a valuation was put on them); and it was of course especially gratifying for a host to be able to present to his guests fish of several varieties from his very own ponds.[41]

Salted seafish, whether wet or dry salted, cost less than fresh seafish in the markets because they remained edible for so much longer. One of the cheapest forms of preserved seafish was stockfish, which was not even salted but was cured by wind-drying alone, and was noted for its hardness. It was a convenient food for servants in large households and for monks in monasteries, but its preparation was highly labour-intensive. In the kitchen inventory of Durham Priory for 1459–60 were included '2 Betynghamyrs pro le Stokfyssh'; and the general advice was to beat the fish for at least an hour, and then to soak it for at least two.[42] After that it could be boiled and eaten with butter or with mustard. It even appeared from time to time on the tables of the nobility, with its flavour submerged in a stew of eels, parsley and onions in a spicy, wine-based broth.[43] Stockfish was so widely consumed, however, that during the later Middle Ages there was a separate Company of Stockfishmongers to control the trade. The Company existed alongside the Company of Saltfishmongers, and the two eventually merged in 1536.

**Cereals and pulses in the Middle Ages**

Cereals, peas and beans, dried and kept through the year, were the main standby for the bread and pottage of the peasant families. Their bread was made of maslin (a mixture of wheat and rye in various proportions) or, in some parts of the country, of rye alone, or of barley. In the Pennines and in Scotland, oats were the breadcorn. When cereals were scarce, beans, peas and bran were used to bulk out the flour, or even to replace the breadcorn altogether.

The well-to-do ate fine wheaten bread, known as pandemain and later, manchet. Their cooks cooked with wheatflour, and for the smoothest pottages, a special kind of prepared wheatflour called 'amidon'. This was the old Roman *amulum*, a starch thickener: its preparation was described by Cato – the flour of hard wheat soaked for ten days in changes of water, then squeezed through a new linen cloth and dried in the sun. The medieval recipe was very similar.[44] The resultant starch product was stored in a dry place for use as a thickener, especially for the white pottages such as blancmange.

The danger that peas and beans might sprout if not kept in suitable conditions still hovered, and could be a threat to the supplies of the manorial household as well as to those in the peasant's hut. A fifteenth-century recipe for preserving beans by turning them into 'canebens' begins:

> Take white beans [of the broad bean family]. Lay
> them in water running two days, and change the
> water. Take them & lay them [to] dry, then dry them
> hard upon a stone or upon an oast. Then shell them
> in a mill [i.e. a handmill], and do away the hulls; and
> cleave the beans [in] 3 or 4 at the most. And then
> make them clean. And so may thou keep them as
> long as thou wilt.[45]

The option of drying the beans upon a heated hearthstone, and the milling of them in a handmill suggests that this operation was carried out at home at all levels of society. For the peasant, peas, beans or canebens were made into pottages with onions, herbs and sometimes a little bacon. In the well-to-do family, canebens were cooked as a thick pottage and eaten with ribs of bacon, or they were made into a sweet dish for Lent, boiled with almond milk and sugar. A similar sweet pottage was made with white peas.[46]

**Sugar, spices and dried fruits in the Middle Ages** Sugar and almonds were two of the imported luxury foods which distinguished the cookery of the noble or wealthy manorial family from that of lowlier folk. These were not foods to ward off famine, but appetising extras – though sugar, initially regarded as a medicine, soon became valued as a preserving agent for fresh fruits. Other expensive imported goods were oriental spices, the rice introduced by the Arabs into southern Europe, and dried fruits: raisins, Greek currants (known as raisins of Corinth) and Damascus prunes. All were carried to ports in southern England on the Italian spice ships; the rice and dried fruits, like the spices, were marketed by the grocers, and they appear together on the spice accounts of well-to-do households. All were kept safely locked up, and issued in small amounts only to the head cook. Care was needed in their storage if they were to remain in good condition; and there is an interesting directive for the Clerk of the Kitchen in the Marquis of Donegal's household book of 1605 which runs:

> He is to receive all provisions of spice made by the Steward or Comptroller, and those to keep: fruit, as currants, raisins, prunes, dates, &c. in some reasonable moist place, for else they will dry away; and the dry spices, as sugar, cinnamon, &c. to be kept dry, for that moisture will decay and greatly waste them and so become in time not serviceable.[47]

The reference to a moist place for housing dried fruit is a reminder that medieval fruits were sun-dried to a very much greater degree of dryness and hardness than our dried fruits today which, until very recently, were partly preserved by a coating of mineral oil (and are now treated with various types of vegetable oil). The hard, dry surface of the medieval fruits acted as a deterrent to insects, moulds and other sources of decay.

Finally, mention must be made of alcoholic drinks, the wine consumed by those of higher estate, and the more plebeian ale, and the manner in which they were conserved. Alcohol is, of course, a powerful preservative in itself. But both wine-making methods and ale-making methods were much less precise than they have now become, and because of variations in the raw materials, in the quality of yeasts, and in the temperatures at which the fermenting processes

**Wine and ale in the Middle Ages**

were carried out, the final products were also very variable. Ale was often made with the malt of mixed cereals until barley prevailed, and it could turn out to be cloudy or ropy. Before the advent of hopped beer it was inclined to sour quickly. Wine could be acid and raw, and was nearly always drunk too young, no more than a year old and usually less, for it soon deteriorated, being attacked in the cask by vinegar bacteria and moulds. Wines from English vineyards were particularly unreliable. Some years the grapes did not ripen at all, and the whole crop had to be turned into verjuice, a kind of sharp vinegar made from unripe grapes or crab-apples.

The response of both wine-makers and ale-makers was to add spices or herbs which not only concealed curious and unpalatable flavours in their beverages, but in some cases did actually hold back for a while the natural causes of decay. Pepper, and from the thirteenth century onwards the fiery grains of paradise imported from West Africa, were put into ale by the alehouse-keepers, or they added herbs such as rosemary or wormwood to it.[48] The keeping properties of the drink were improved when beer made with hops was introduced from the Flemish Netherlands in the fourteenth century. Herbal ales of many different kind continued to be widely consumed in northern England until very much later; some of the herbs added to them were valued for their medicinal properties.

Spiced wines had been made in Roman times. Often honey was added to the wine-must, to help to feed the yeasts as it fermented. Spiced and sweetened wines continued to be made in France (under the name of *piment*), and were reintroduced from there after the Norman Conquest. Hippocras, the wine drunk at the end of a feast as a digestive, was only spiced and sweetened shortly before it was served out, but for other spiced or herbed wines, the additions were made while the wine was in cask, and some of them did help to preserve it for longer in a drinkable state. Sage wine, a favourite of King Edward I, was a case in point: sage was believed to restore ill-smelling wines, and its essential oil did, in fact, have a helpful antiseptic effect.

Wine, like vinegar, could be employed in the making of preserves. Honey and spices, wine and vinegar all went into a kind of chutney of cut up boiled roots and pears with currants called 'compost'. It was stored in earthenware pots for long keeping; 'and take of it when thou wilt, and serve forth'.[49] Vinegar was both a condiment and a preservative, used with brine to make pickling liquids for fish such as pickled herrings, and the sousing drink for brawn. The poor man's vinegar was alegar or eisel, based upon ale-wort as vinegar was based upon wine-must.

The role of the imported spices and sugar in preserving was an ever-growing one. Spices improved both the keeping quality of brine and vinegar pickling liquids, and also the flavour they imparted. Sugar made it possible to preserve fruits at times of glut, and to keep them for consumption in winter and spring. Both made available a huge range of new cooked dishes, sauces and confections. But here we begin to leave the domain of foodstuffs preserved in the season of glut against the season of famine, and to enter that of luxury foods, appetisers, relishes, 'sugared delicates' for the banquet, and other tasty morsels – food delights rather than food necessities. That is another and different chapter in the history of food preservation.

1. K. Williamson, *The Atlantic Islands* (London, 1948), p. 82.
2. Some of the sets of postholes found on early archaeological sites could have held supports for such shelters.
3. M. Martin, *A Description of the Western Islands of Scotland c. 1695, and A Late Voyage to St. Kilda . . . 1698*, ed. D. J. McLeod (Stirling, 1934), pp. 441; 456.
4. ibid., p. 200.
5. G. Landt, *A Description of the Feroe Islands* (London, 1810), p. 384.
6. ibid., p. 356; Williamson, p. 29.
7. Williamson, p. 29.
8. A. Riddervold, 'Gravlax, the buried salmon' in *Oxford*

**Notes and References**

*Symposium on Food and Cookery 1984 and 1985, Proceedings*,
ed. T. Jaine (London, 1986), pp. 126; 130.

9. Williamson, p. 82.

10. C. B. Hieatt & S. Butler, eds., *Curye on Inglysch* (Early English
Text Society, SS 8, 1985), II, no. 58; Sir H. Platt, *Jewel House of
Art and Nature*, new ed. (London, 1653), p. 20.

11. R. A. S. Macalistair, *The Archaeology of Ireland* (London, 1928),
p. 192.

12. J. Ritchie, 'A keg of butter from Skye', *Procs. Soc. Antiquaries of
Scotland* 75 (1940), pp. 5-22, espec. p. 9. The burial of butter is
still practised in several countries around the world, e.g. Kashmir
where 'the older the butter, the greater the luxury'.

13. L. Debes, *Description of the Feroes* (London, 1676), p. 263.

14. Sir L. Scott, 'Gallo-British colonies', *Procs. Prehist. Soc.* 14
(1948), pp. 124-5; Martin, p. 434.

15. Martin, p. 159.

16. P. J. Reynolds, 'Experimental Iron Age storage pits: an interim
report', *Procs. Prehist. Soc.* 40 (1974), pp. 118-31.

17. G. Bersu, 'Excavations at Little Woodbury, Wilts.', *Procs.
Prehist. Soc.* 6 (1940), p. 62.

18. S. S. Frere, *Britannia*, 3rd ed. (London, 1987), pp. 270-1; C. A.
Wilson, *Food and Drink in Britain* (London, 1973), p. 235. Corn
was also kiln-dried in medieval Ireland: see N. Edwards, *The
Archaeology of Early Medieval Ireland* (London, 1990), pp. 62-3.

19. H. L. Movius, 'A Neolithic site on the River Bann', *Procs. Roy.
Irish Acad.* 43C (1935-37), pp. 17-40.

20. Columella, 7.8.7.

21. Wilson, p. 19.

22. A. K. Bowman & J. D. Thomas, *Vindolanda: the Latin Writing
Tablets* (Britannia monograph 4, 1983), pp. 93-6.

23. As late as the 1880s, milk put into the crogan, the traditional
pottery container then still in regular use in the remoter parts of
Scotland, was flavoured by organic residues. The taste of sweet
milk was 'thus unfamiliar to the people who come to like best
what they know best, and to prefer what is unpalatable to us',
according to an account written in 1880 (A. Mitchell, *The Past
in the Present*, Edinburgh, 1880, p. 45) quoted by H. Cheape,
'Food and liquid containers in the Hebrides', in *Food and Drink
and Travelling Accessories*, ed. A. Fenton & J. Myrdal
(Edinburgh, 1988), p. 22.

24. V. Cheke, *The Story of Cheese-making in Britain* (London,
1959), p. 66.

25. Columella, 7.8.

26. G. Gow, 'Making butter in the Ceilidh-house', *Tocher* 36 (1981),
p. 38 quoted by H. Cheape in Fenton & Myrdal (1988), p. 19.

27. J. Myrdal, 'The Plunge-churn from Ireland to Tibet', in Fenton &
Myrdal (1988), pp. 111-37.

28. Herodotus, 4.2.

29. Hieatt & Butler, II, no. 58: in the recipe 'For to do away reesting
of venison' the instructions are first that it should be buried in

earth for three days, and then: 'Frot [rub] it well with great salt of
poite [saltpetre] there where the reesting is, & after let it hang in
rain water all night or more'.

30. *Walter of Henley*, ed. D. Oschinsky (Oxford, 1971), p. 337,
    c.99–100.
31. B. James & A. M. Robinson, *Clarendon Place . . . a Mediaeval
    Palace and Hunting Lodge near Salisbury, Wilts.* (Society of
    Antiquaries report 45, 1988), pp. 23; 88–9; 269.
32. Hieatt & Butler, II, no. 57.
33. R. de Swinfield, *Roll of the Household Expenses . . . 1289 and
    1290*, ed. J. Webb (Camden Society publications 59 & 62, 1853–
    4), pp. cvii; cxcvi; ccxxiii.
34. W. Langland, *Piers Plowman*, A. text, ed. G. Kane (London,
    1960), passus 7, lines 265–9.
35. Clarified butter was used especially in the cooking of sweet,
    meatless dishes, e.g. T. Austin, ed. *Two Fifteenth-century
    Cookery-books* (Early English Text Society, OS 91, 1888), pp. 42;
    53; 83; 98.
36. Wardrobe accounts of Edward I, quoted in *Our English Home*
    (London, 1860), p. 66; J. M. Steane, 'The royal fishponds of
    medieval England', in *Medieval Fish, Fisheries and Fishponds in
    England*, ed. M. Astin (British Archaeological Reports, British
    series 182, 1988), vol. 1, p. 49.
37. For further information on 'greenfish', 'saltfish' and the herring
    industry, see C. L. Cutting, *Fish Saving* (London, 1955).
38. *The Regulations and Establishment of the Household of Henry
    Algernon Percy, the fifth Earl of Northumberland . . . 1512*
    (London, new edn. 1905), pp. 78–9.
39. *The Boke of Kervynge*, ed. F. J. Furnivall (Early English Text
    Society, OS 32, 1868), p. 166.
40. M. N. LaBarge, *A Baronial Household of the Thirteenth Century*
    (London, 1965), p. 80.
41. F. Dyer, 'The consumption of freshwater fish in medieval
    England', in *Medieval Fish, Fisheries and Fishponds . . .* (1988),
    vol. 1, pp. 31–3.
42. C. J. Bond, 'Monastic fisheries', in *Medieval Fish, Fisheries and
    Fishponds . . .* (1988), vol. 1, p. 73; *The Goodman of Paris*, ed. &
    trans. E. Power (London, 1928), p. 273.
43. Austin, p. 10.
44. Cato, 87; Austin, p. 112.
45. C. B. Hieatt, ed., *An Ordinance of Pottage . . . the Fifteenth-
    century Culinary Recipes in Yale University MS Beinecke 163*
    (London, 1988), p. 36, no. 2.
46. ibid., p. 36, nos. 3 and 4; Hieatt & Butler, IV, no. 72.
47. 'A Breviate touching the order and government of a Nobleman's
    House, 1605', communicated by Sir J. Banks, *Archaeologia* 13
    (1800), p. 315.
48. Wilson, pp. 373–4.
49. Hieatt & Butler, IV, no. 103.

# 3.

## *Pots for Potting: English Pottery and its Role in Food Preservation in the Post-Medieval Period*

PETER BREARS

Many of today's forms of food-packing, including tin cans, foil trays, collapsible metal tubes, glass jars, plastic tubs and vacuum-packs, all employ the same basic principle: that suitably prepared food can remain in good condition over prolonged periods if it is kept in completely air-tight conditions. In Britain this principle was already well-understood during the medieval period, when containers ranged from pie-crusts to skins and bladders.

In the late fifteenth century, however, this country's pottery industry entered on a prolonged phase of expansion, during which it improved the quality of its wares, especially with regard to glazing, and greatly extended the range of its products. To its old-established trade in jugs, cooking pots, bowls, and a few other domestic wares, it added cups, taken over from the coopers, plates, new forms of cooking vessels and jars etc, some of which were ideally designed for the preservation of food. So useful were these new earthenwares that by 1569 the term 'potting' had been adopted to describe the whole process of preserving foods, especially fish and meats, by sealing them in airtight containers.[1] In the following pages we shall trace the development and use of pots for potting over the past four hundred years, but, before that, we need to describe their predecessors, the pasties and pies of medieval England.

So long as pottery remained absorbent, poorly glazed, fairly brittle, and small in scale, strong crusts of rye or wheat flour provided excellent containers in which meat and fish could be baked, sealed with butter, transported, and stored ready for use. Of all the pasties made in the medieval period, those of venison were the most significant, for as Andrew Boorde commented, venison 'is a lordes dysshe, . . . good for an Englysshe man, for it doth anymate him to be as he is, which is, stronge and hardy.' They were served on Christmas Day, at weddings, royal entertainments, and at dinner-parties. In 'The Merry Wives of Windsor', for example, Master Page invited Justice Shallow, Sir John Falstaff and their various companions to his house, where 'we have a hot venison pasty to dinner'. Similarly 4,000 'Pasties of Venison colde' and 1,500 'Hot pasties of Venison' were served at the gargantuan feast held at Cawood in the West Riding of Yorkshire in 1465 to celebrate the enthronement of Archbishop Neville.[2]

**Pasties and Pies**

One of the earliest recipes appears in the British Museum's Harleian Manuscript No. 4016;

Venyson ybaked
Take haunches of venyson, parboile it in faire water
and salt; then take faire paast, and ley there-on the
Venyson y-cutte in pieces as thou wolt have it, and
cast under hit, and above hit, powder of ginger, or
peper and salt medylde togidre, And sette in An
oven, and lete hem bake til they be ynogh.

Similar recipes, using either raw or parboiled venison, continue to appear in recipe books up to the mid-eighteenth century, the later authors including Charles Carter (1730) and Richard Bradley (1736).

The size and construction of these thick-walled pasties is difficult to establish, but Hoefnagel's painting of 'The Marriage Feast at Bermondsey' of the late sixteenth century shows a processional party of serving maids and men leaving the cook-shop, each apparently carrying a large oval venison pasty vertically in front of them, the weight being taken by large napkins tied around their necks. In 1736, however, Bradley was recommending that 'the Carver ought always to take the Services of the Pasty from the Corners where the Fat is, to do honour to the Master and his Park', which suggests a more rectangular form.[3] They were usually glazed, or 'endored' with egg yolk, with melted butter or beer.

A similar method of making butter-sealed pastry cases was used to preserve the long-celebrated Severn lampreys, the favourite dish of Henry III, while they were in transit from Gloucester to London. One late fourteenth- or early fifteenth-century recipe details how the lamprey should be cleaned, and put in a 'paste of dow' with good spicery and bread tempered with its blood, with wine or vinegar, before being baked.[4] A fifteenth-century version, meanwhile, instructs the cook to place the same contents in

> fair round coffins of fine paste . . . Then cover it
> fairly with a lid, save a little hole in the middle, and
> at that hole blow in the coffin with thy mouth a
> good blast of wind. And suddenly stop up the hole,
> that the wind abide within, to raise up the coffin
> that it fall not down. And when it is a little hardened
> in the oven, prick the coffin with a pin stuck on a
> rod's end for [fear] of braking the coffin, and then
> let it bake and serve forth cold.[5]

By the mid-seventeenth century, the people of Gloucester were adopting pottery vessels too, the cleaned and seasoned lampreys now being laid 'round in a Pot or strong crust upon a good Lare of Butter, and store of Onions' with more butter added, and a lid, before being baked for three or four hours or more. On cooling, three-fingers breadth of melted butter was then poured upon the fish, so that they would keep a year, 'so the Butter be not opened, nor

craked, that the air get into the fish'.[6] Ceremonial lamprey
pies are still made by the City of Gloucester for presentation
to the Sovereign on important occasions; one was presented
to Her Majesty to celebrate her Jubilee in 1977, having
travelled up to London in the Mayoral limousine.[7] Other
dishes which continued this medieval tradition include the
goose pies, or Yorkshire Christmas pies, which were still
being made in the late nineteenth century.

In its simpler form, the goose pie was made by baking
boned and seasoned geese in a raised piecrust which was
then filled with clarified butter to exclude the air. For
richer varieties a number of birds were boned and wrapped
one around another; first a pigeon, then a partridge, then a
fowl, then a goose, and finally a turkey, thus forming a
solid mass of delicate meat. This was then enclosed within
a thick, raised piecrust, with hare, woodcock, moor-game
and a large quantity of butter, before being sent to the
oven. As Hannah Glasse noted, the crust would take a
bushel of flour and since 'These pies are often sent to
London in a box, as presents; therefore the walls must be
well built'. This factor was very important; one large
Christmas pie sent from Sheffield to Lord Brougham in
1832 failed to arrive safely, since it broke down under its
own weight while still in transit. The appearance of these
pies is clearly recorded in a painting by Mary Ellen Best of
1839, and in an illustration in Charles Francatelli's *The
Modern Cook* of 1855. They are extremely ornate, their
crusts being covered with strips or stamped-out details of
applied pastry decoration.[8]

Although it is difficult to obtain direct documentary
evidence, it is probable that these strong, thick crusts were
chiefly considered as a means of containing the contents
during the baking and subsequent storage or transport,
rather than as forming an intentionally edible portion of
the pie. This is certainly suggested by continental paintings
such as Jan Steen's 'The Fat Kitchen', where fingers and
spoons are being used to scoop out the contents of a large

**3.**
Pasties and pies.
Pastry crusts provided
very convenient
containers for the
cooking and short-
term preservation of
meat and fish. Seen
here are (A) late
sixteenth century
venison pasties from
Hoefnagel's *Marriage
Feast at Bermondsey*;
(B) eating from a pie-
crust from Jan
Steen's *Fat Kitchen*,
mid seventeenth
century; (C) & (D)
fourteenth century
flampoyntes of pork;
(E) a medieval chewet
of pork and chicken
baked in a coffin; and
(F) & (G) Yorkshire
Christmas pies of
1855 and 1839.

pie, while one of Pieter Claesz' still lifes shows a spoon
resting by the rich filling spilling out from a broken
piecrust.

The pork pies, still to be found in butchers' shops, supermarkets, market cafés and public houses throughout the country, remain as popular as ever. They have a long history, being descended from the 'flampoyntes' or 'chewetes' of the early medieval period. Two recipes for flampoyntes dating from the fourteenth century describe how the pounded paste of pork, mixed with cheese and spices, was enclosed within a crust decorated either with standing points cut from the lid of the pie itself, or made separately, fried, and embedded in the surface of the pork before baking. Chewetes, meanwhile, could be made from chopped pork and chicken baked in 'a coffyn as to a pye smale'.[9] Here the crust appears to have formed an important edible element of the pie, however, keeping the moist meat clean, and enabling it to be readily eaten with the fingers. It is these properties, rather than those of direct preservation, which have ensured its continuing success.

**Potting-Pots**

From the Elizabethan period the pastry pie-case was largely replaced by the earthenware pot as a container for meats or fish preserved under a layer of clarified butter. Writing in 1669, for example, Sir Kenelm Digby advised the use of 'a Pot or strong crust' for preserving, while later writers recommend the use of a pot almost excusively.[10] Since the joints or fillets were baked whole beneath a temporary pastry lid, the pots had to be of a suitable size to take an entire haunch of venison etc. On being taken out of the oven, the pastry lid might be removed and replaced with a weighted trencher until all was cold, when a layer of melted butter was added. Some of the pots had straight, slightly conical sides, so that the meat could be turned out on a plate ready to be served at table.[11]

In some areas, the potting of joints of meat was still being carried out early this century, Mr Wood of Slaidburn recording that pork and all mutton, except the legs, were treated in this way in his part of rural eastern Lancashire.

The meat was preserved by 'cutting into small pieces, plunging in a crock, salting, and putting in the oven. The fat melts and covers the whole. Every month or so when the oven was hot the crock would be heated up afresh. Often in his young days they would do this with a pig killed at the fall [autumn] and it would be kept on until harvest time [late summer]. From time to time pieces would be removed and consumed'.[12] Presumably some of the strong cylindrical black-glazed red earthenware pots made in the small potteries around Cliviger (near Burnley), Burton-in-Lonsdale and Halifax were used for this purpose.

In a similar manner, finely-flavoured fish such as the char of the Lake District were filleted and potted in butter in specially-made char-pots from the early eighteenth century, as the accounts of the Taylors of Finsthwaite illustrate (note the farthing column following the pence column):[13]

'Feb 9th 1731 act. of money laid out for bro.

| William Taylor as follows: | £ | s | d | [f] |
|---|---|---|---|---|
| Imprs. two Charr Pots | 0 | 1 | 3 | 0 |
| Do. 4 doz of Charrs at 5s per Doz | 1 | 0 | 0 | 0 |
| Seasoning for the same – | | | | |
| Mace 1oz qr. | 0 | 1 | 10 | 2 |
| Clovs. 1 & ½ | 0 | 1 | 1 | 2 |
| Sinom. 1 & ½ | 0 | 1 | 1 | 2 |
| Blackpeper | 0 | 0 | 3 | 0 |
| Carre. to Daventry at 2d. pr lb. w. 29 lb. | 0 | 5 | 0 | 0 |

The pots certainly assisted the profitable despatch of the preserved char to distant consumers. The Duke of Montagu wrote to Mr Atkinson of Dalton in Furness on January 27th, 1738, about the 'Pott of Charr which you sent by that day's carrier, which was the best I ever eat and I would have you send me some of the same by every Carryer, take care to Pick the hen fish and those that are of the Red

Kind, and let them be potted and seasoned just as that Pot was for it can't be beter'.[14] The pots themselves were most frequently made in tin-glazed earthenware, or delft-ware, at the Liverpool potteries, the vertical walls of their broad, shallow bodies being decorated with representations of chars executed in bold, colourful brushwork. When most of the delftware potteries closed in Liverpool in the 1770s, similar vessels were made in creamware as evidenced by an example now in the Castle Museum at York. It is probable that this shape of potting-pot had been introduced to Liverpool by the London potters who established themselves in the great Lancashire port in 1712, for very similar pots have been excavated from the site of the Norfolk House pottery of 1680–1737 in Lambeth.[15] About the same time, in the early eighteenth century, potting-pots of identical shape, but coated in a brown manganese-speckled glaze, were being produced in the Staffordshire potteries, examples being found in a 1740s context at Temple Balsall in Warwickshire.[16]

By the early eighteenth century it had been realised that potting was much more successful if the meat, fish or cheese had first been finely chopped or beaten to a smooth paste in a mortar before being packed into the pot. In 1747, for example, Hannah Glasse advised that lobster should be boiled, cleaned and seasoned, then 'beat to a Paste, put into your Potting-pot, and put it down as close and hard as you can' before sealing with clarified butter.[17] This is the method which is still being used today for the commercial preparation of meat and fish pastes.

The traditional form of shallow, round potting-pot continued in domestic use up to about the time of the Second World War, the majority of them being made in the industrial potteries of the north of England and the north Midlands. The stoneware examples made in the Chesterfield area were particularly attractive with their moulded decoration of sheep, trees, etc., and small lion-mask handles.[18]

Perhaps the most important manufacturer of these open-topped pots for retail use was C. T. Maling who set up the Ford (A) Pottery at Ouseburn near Newcastle-upon-Tyne in 1859.[19] Here eighty tons of clay were processed into three-quarters of a million vessels every month, the majority being jam and meat-paste pots made for a vast number of small shopkeepers. The pots usually bear transfer-printed names such as:

'ALFRED CRABTREE/BUTCHER/MARKET
PLACE/HECKMONDWIKE'
'HAMPTON/PASTRY COOK &
CONFECTIONER/22–23 COPTHALL AVENUE
& 19 MOORGATE EC'
'OLDHAM & SONS, NEWARK, POTTED BEEF'
(this in a Garter cartouche), or
'SNELLING'S/CHICKEN & HAM/RAMPANT
HORSE ST. NORWICH' (with Willow-pattern
borders)

Smaller potteries were also involved in this trade. Clokie's of Castleford, for example, made round and oval potting-pots with flaring conical sides up to the 1950s, the names of the local meat-paste manufacturers being printed in underglaze colour around the broad, flat rim using specially-designed rubber stamps.

The rapid expansion of the railway network in the second quarter of the nineteenth century greatly facilitated the movement of both new potting-pots to the manufacturers, and pre-packed potted meats and pastes to distant retailers. This meant that locally-produced delicacies which had formerly enjoyed only a limited market, due to expensive transport costs, could now be cheaply distributed to most parts of the country. Major grocery and provision merchants could now greatly expand their business activities, and companies such as the Army and Navy Stores, Burgess', Crosse & Blackwell, Fortnum & Mason, etc., were thus

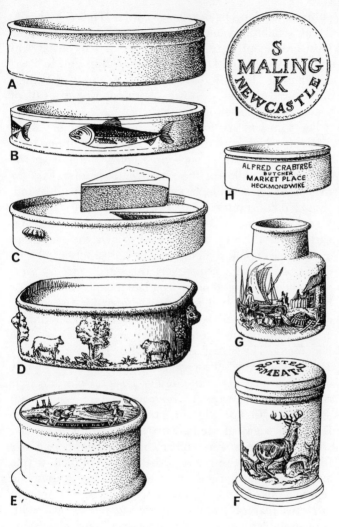

**4.**
Potting pots. Vessels used to pot meat or fish: (A) seventeenth century delftware pot from Norfolk House, Lambeth; (B) an eighteenth century Liverpool delftware char pot; (C) an earthenware shrimp-paste pot, early twentieth century; (D) a Derbyshire brown saltglazed stoneware potting pot, early twentieth century; (E) an 1840s transfer-printed earthenware shrimp-paste pot showing Pegwell Bay, Ramsgate; (F) a transfer-printed potted meat jar showing wild deer, after Sir Edwin Landseer, made by F. R. Pratt & Co., c.1865; (G) a transfer-printed earthenware fishpaste jar made by Bates, Brown-Westhead, Moore & Co., c.1860; (H) meat-paste pot made by C. T. Maling of Newcastle-upon-Tyne, late nineteenth century, and (I) the mark on the base of Maling's jars.

enabled to move into the truly national markets which they continue to serve today.

For this trade, a variety of relatively new forms of potting-pot were developed in the 1830s and 40s by large potteries working in Burslem, Fenton, Hanley, Stoke-on-Trent, Coalbrookdale and Stockton-on-Tees. Of these, the most prominent were the firm of T., J. and J. Mayer of Furlong Works and Dale Hall Pottery, Burslem; R. Pratt of Fenton; John Ridgway, Bates & Co., and their successors; and Bates, Brown-Westhead, Moore & Co., of Cauldon Place, Shelton, Hanley.

For potted meats, they produced cylindrical jars about 3¾ inches high with pronounced mouldings around their rims and bases, this shape probably deriving from the delftware albarellos of the seventeenth century. Jars for fish paste, meanwhile, usually took the form of round-shouldered cylindrical jars with tall cylindrical necks measuring some 3–4 inches overall, their bases being particularly thick or hollow-based to give the maximum appearance of bulk combined with minimal actual volume. Their bodies were attractively decorated with transfer-printed designs based on appropriate themes (wild deer or boar-hunts for potted meats, fishermen for fish pastes, etc.); or on foreign landscapes (Venice, Constantinople etc.), or on popular contemporary events, such as 'The Landing Of The British Army At The Crimea' in the early 1850s. Their chief decoration appeared across the slightly domed surface of their circular lids, to which colour transfer prints of extremely high quality were applied from around 1850. For the shrimp pastes of Pegwell Bay, Ramsgate, views of the bay, its well-known locations and shrimping scenes were shown, but soon the pot-lid was illustrating everything from artistic groups of shells to fine architectural prospects, lively contemporary scenes and reproductions of popular paintings. The pot lid grew so attractive that it became a collector's item in its own right, good examples commanding high prices in today's antique trade. Anyone interested in obtaining further information on the subject should consult its standard work, C. Williams-Wood's *Staffordshire Pot Lids and their Potters* (1972), which traces the development, designs and dates of these vessels in considerable detail.

At the end of the nineteenth century the manufacture of this form of potting-pot went into a rapid decline as its place was taken by mass-produced glass jars. Shallow round pots continued to be made for the sale of high quality anchovy pastes up to a few years ago, however, when they were replaced by white plastic pots of identical form. Elsenham's *Patum Peperium* of 1828 thus continues the English potting-pot tradition in the form of its containers, albeit with the inevitable change to a new material. But even this is under pressure as anchovy paste is now being packed for the ultimate in convenience in metal tubes, like paint or toothpaste.

The preservation of flesh by impregnating it with salt has been practised in this country ever since the Iron Age.[20] It provided one of the most important and widespread methods of keeping meat and fish in a good, edible condition throughout the long winter months from that time, some 2,500 years ago, through to the late nineteenth century when alternative techniques became widely available. Even so, hams and bacon etc., continue to be prepared by salting, for the flavour salt gives is still greatly appreciated.

**Pots for Salting**

Salting was such a common, everyday occurrence in medieval Britain that, as with brewing and baking, the cooks of the period never had need to record their methods in recipe books. From the early post-medieval period, however, numerous recipes survive in both manuscript and printed sources. In general terms, the larger joints of beef and sides of bacon were salted in wooden tubs, while from the seventeenth century at least pork, hams and tongues could also be salted in purposely-made glazed earthenware pans. In 1681, for example, Rebecca Price of Westbury in Buckinghamshire was laying tongues covered

43

in salt 'on a pan' for a month at a time, while 'cloughs to salt meat in' were being made at Oakley Bank in Northamptonshire in 1712.[21] For pickling tongues, or joints of pork or beef, the pans were oval or round in design, with vertical sides, glazed interiors and rims, and perhaps a couple of strong handles for lifting. They appear in the catalogues and price lists of a number of nineteenth-century coarse earthenware potteries, having been made in these establishments, and many others, for many years;[22]

Tongue Pots
    Brede Pottery, Sussex, c. 1840, 5s., 8s., 11s., & 15s. per dozen.
    Silverhill Pottery, Sussex, 1846, 6d. to 1s. 6d. each.
    Bridge Pottery, Sunderland, 1883, 2s. to 3s. 6d. each.
    Walker's Pottery, Thornaby on Tees, 1894, 9d. to 1s. 6d. each.
    Doulton's Sunderland Ware, 1s. 8d. to 4s. 3d. each and also from 1 gallon at 1s. 6d. to 22 gallons at 33s.

Beef Pans
    Brede Pottery, Sussex, c. 1840, 1s. 4d., 2s., 2s. 9d., & 4s. 6d. each.
    Pearson & Co., Whittington Moor Pottery, Derbyshire, c. 1940, 1 to 18 pints at 2s. 2d. to 39s. for twelve.

In use, they could be employed for either salting or brining. Although there are many individual recipes, the following, taken from the 1861 edition of *Mrs Beeton's Book of Household Management* are typical;

833.   To Pickle Pork
Ingredients ¼ lb of saltpetre; salt.
Mode. – As pork does not keep long without being salted, cut it into pieces of a suitable size as soon as the pig is cold. Rub the pieces well with salt, and put

## Pots for Potting

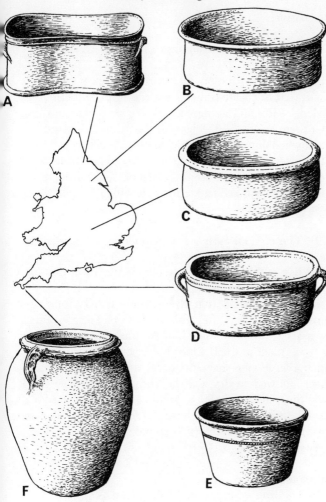

**5.**
Salting pots. These Victorian glazed earthenware vessels were all used for salting, the first group being made to hold tongues or joints of pork (A) coming from Scott's Pottery, Sunderland, c.1880; (B) from West Yorkshire; (C) from Oxfordshire, and (D) from Cornwall. The salt-glazed beef-pot (E) was made early this century by Pearson & Co., Whittington Moor, Derbyshire, in sizes from 1 to 18 pints, while the earthenware bussa (F), used for salting pilchards, comes from western Cornwall.

them in a pan with a sprinkling of it between each piece: as it melts on the top, strew on more. Lay a coarse cloth over the pan, a board over that, and a weight on the board, to keep the pork down in the brine. If excluded from the air, it will continue good for nearly 2 years.

Alternatively:

641.   A Pickle for Tongues or Beef (Newmarket
Recipe)
Ingredients. – 1 gallon of soft water, 3 lbs of coarse
salt, 6 oz of coarse brown sugar, ½ oz of saltpetre.
Mode. – Put all the ingredients in a saucepan, and
let them boil ½ hour, clear off the scum as it rises,
and when done pour the pickle into a pickling pan.
Let it get cold, then put in the meat, and allow it to
remain in the pickle from 8 to 14 days, according to
the size. It will keep good for 6 months if boiled
once a fortnight . . .

(N.B. These recipes are not recommended for present day
use.)

For hams, the pans were almost identical to those used
for pickling tongues, except that they were pear-shaped in
design. This was so that they closely fitted around the
hams, minimising the amount of pickling solution
necessary for total submersion. An interesting alternative
form was made at the Buckley Potteries in North Wales, in
which a large vase-shaped pot was thrown on the potter's
wheel, allowed to dry a little, and then sliced vertically
down the middle in order to produce two ham-shaped pans
(see Figure 6A). Being both large in size and time-
consuming in manufacture, ham pans were comparatively
expensive;[23]

Ham Pans
    Brede Pottery, Sussex, c. 1840, 2s. 6d. & 3s. 6d.
          common ditto, 1s. 6d. & 2s. 6d.
    Silverhill Pottery, Sussex, 1845, 3s. each.
    Bridge Pottery, Sunderland, 1883, 2s. to 3s. 6d.
          each.
    Walker's Pottery, Thornaby-on-Tees, 1894, 2s. to
          3s. 6d. each.

Doulton's Sunderland Ware, 1921, 3s. 4d. to
    5s. 10d., also 1 gallon at 1s. 6d. to 12 gallons
    at 15s.

Again, there were many individual recipes and regional
variations in methods of curing hams, but in general, wet-
curing entails a prolonged immersion in a saline pickle,
perhaps preceded by a period of dry-salting, sometimes
under pressure, to remove body fluids which would inhibit
preservation. These processes are detailed in the following
recipe quoted in Florence White's *Good Things in England*
of 1932;

A Very Special Recipe for Pickling Hams
Ingredients: Bay salt 1 lb; common salt 1 lb; moist
sugar 2 lb; saltpetre 4 oz; salt prunella 2 oz; juniper
berries ¼ lb; bay leaves 3; thyme, sweet basil,
marjoram, sweetbriar, tarragon; a sprig of each; a
few whole peppercorns and allspice; 1 quart of the
strongest old ale.
                    Method.      [abstract]
1.  Rub hams with common salt.
2.  Press with one hundredweight, between boards,
    for 24 hours.
3.  Bruise juniper berries, and boil with all
    ingredients (except herbs) for 20 minutes, allow
    to cool until the hands can be put in the pickle.
4.  Wipe the hams, place on the herbs in pan, and
    pour the pickle over all.
5.  Rub the pickle into the hams, turning and
    basting them every day for a month.
6.  Remove the hams, dry them, and smoke them as
    necessary.

By placing the hams on lengths of wood bridging across
the ham-pans, the waste juices could be collected during
the initial pressing, while the ham-pans themselves

**6.**
These glazed earthen-
ware pans were
specially shaped to
hold a complete ham
and its preserving
brine. They come
from (A) Buckley
Pottery, North Wales;
(B) Scott's Pottery,
Sunderland, c.1880;
(C) the 18th century
Wedgwood's pottery,
Coxwold, North
Yorkshire (?); (D)
one of the Halifax
potteries, c.1900; (E)
Oxburgh Hall,
Norfolk, pre 1838,
and (F) Brede Pottery,
Sussex. Over the pan
shown in (G) is the
ham being given its
initial pressing to
remove the body-
fluids.

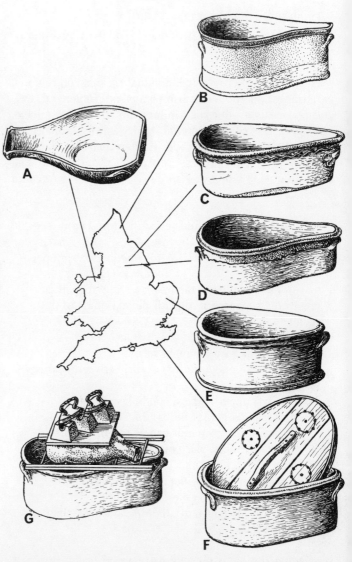

provided ideal containers for the pickling process.[24] Once
the hams were wanted for the table, the ham-pans could
also be used for the eight to twenty-four-hour soaking in

fresh water which usually preceded either boiling or baking.

In nineteenth-century Cornwall, large earthenware jars **Bussas** called bussas were used for the domestic preservation of pilchards. When shoals of these North Atlantic fish arrived on the Cornish coast, they could be caught in large numbers, Frank Buckland's *Natural History of Fishes* of 1883 recording that a single boat once took 80,000 here in a single night. Whenever these gluts occurred at Penzance or Newlyn, the news was passed up to the potters at Truro, who immediately loaded their waggons with a supply of new bussas and raced down to the ports to capture this opportunity for additional sales. Bill Lake told me that his family's pottery had always won the race, since their competitor's horse invariably halted at every public house along the route from sheer force of habit!

In use, the bottom of the bussa was lined with a layer of salt, then a layer of pilchards, this process continuing until the vessel was full. A piece of flannel was then laid across to prevent the fish from going 'rusty', and a heavy stone put on top to press them down into the salt.

Anchovies were also preserved here. One local writer of a century ago commented that they were 'Quite a common fish in Autumn, from Polperro to Falmouth, I have several in salt now'.[25]

Until about the 1960s most households still salted down **Salting** their French beans in the late summer, ready for winter **Vegetables** use. Having been sliced, perhaps with the aid of a hand-operated machine, the beans were packed down into large stoneware jars, the method being almost identical to that described by Hannah Glasse in 1747:[26]

To keep French Beans all the Year
Take fine young Beans, gather them of a very fine
Day, have a large Stone-jarr ready clean and dry, lay

a Layer of Salt at the Bottom, and then a Layer of
Beans, then Salt, and then Beans, and so on till the
Jarr is full, cover them with Salt, tye a coarse Cloth
over them, and a Board on that, and then a Weight
to keep it close from all Air; set them in a dry
Cellar . . .

Most other methods of preserving vegetables required the
use of vinegar. Since this was acid, it would have dissolved
the lead from the glaze of most contemporary earthenware,
with potentially lethal results. It was for this reason that
pickles were usually stored in bottles or jars made of
stoneware or glass.

**Butter Pots**  From the seventeenth century at least, butter was preserved
or packed for sale by being beaten into large pottery vessels,
coarse salt being sprinkled between each layer as it was
firmly knuckled down to exclude all pockets of air. This
process could be subject to considerable frauds or abuses,
however, the pots frequently being laid with good butter
for a little way at the top but with bad at the bottom.
Sometimes the butter was placed in upright rolls, touching
one another at the top to give a solid surface, but leaving
great hollows below, or perhaps the butter was adulterated
with tallow or hogs' lard.[27]

In Staffordshire, in an attempt to prevent these practices,
the authorities insisted that every butter pot had to bear a
mark showing its maker and its weight. As Dr Robert Plot
informs us in his *Natural History of Staffordshire* of 1677,
'The Butter they buy by the *Pot* of a long cylindrical form,
made at *Burslem* in this country of a certain size, so as not
to weigh above six pounds at most, and yet to contain at
least 14 pound of Butter according to an Act of Parliament
made about 14 or 16 years agoe, for regulateing the abuses
of this trade in the making of Pots, and false packing of the
Butter'. The Act referred to (14 Charles II chap. 26 [1662])

50

states that each 'Pott of Butter ought to weigh Twenty pounds viz. Fourteen pounds of good and Merchantable Butter Neat and the Pott Six pounds . . [and] every Potter shall sett upon every Pott which he shall sell for packing up of Butter the just weight which shall be of every such Pot when it is burnt, together with the first Letter of his or theire Christian name and his or theire Sirname at length . . . [and] no Farmer or other person whatsoever shall expose to sale any Butter packed up in any other Pot than such as shall be marked by the Potter as aforesaid . . .'. These pots were apparently purchased chiefly by farmers living within about fifteen to twenty miles of Burslem, for the local Quarter Sessions Rolls included accusations of the use of unlawful pots at Aston, fifteen miles south of Burslem; Cheadle, ten miles to the east; Norton, just to the north-east; and Horton, about eight miles from Burslem in the same direction. The pots were mainly designed for packing butter for the Uttoxeter market, where dealers from London purchased major supplies for consumption in the capital.[28]

The pots themselves were made in a coarse grey-buff ware which was impervious to water, even though unglazed. This property prevented the dealers increasing the weight by soaking them in water just before making a sale. In shape, the Staffordshire butter-pots were cylindrical, with a slight constriction beneath the rim to enable a cover to be tied down across their mouths, the shortest of the three main heights of pot having small horizontal handles for ease of carrying. Writing in 1865, F. Redfern stated that the butter pot trade had died out in Uttoxeter about eighty years earlier.[29] Perhaps his statement relates to new legislation (36 George III c.86) of 1790 by which it was decreed that every vessel made for the packing of butter should be of good well-seasoned wood, marked with the name and, later, the address of the maker. Even though the economic role of the butter-pot finished about this time, pots continued to be used for packing butter for home consumption through to the late nineteenth and early twentieth centuries.

Outside Staffordshire, butter-pots were made in a number of rural potteries. In those of North Devon in the seventeenth century, for example, they were made in a variety of sizes, and documentary references to four hundredweight of butter in eight pots, to pots holding 27 lb, and to 'gallons' of butter probably represent pots with approximately half-hundredweight, quarter, and stone [14 lb] capacities.[30] They were exported from ports such as Bideford to the Glamorgan coast of South Wales and to the west coast of Ireland, from where they returned to Devon full of butter for either local consumption or for transit to more distant markets. Alternatively they were shipped directly from the butter-producing areas to the trans-Atlantic colonies of Maryland, Virginia, or Barbados. In shape, they appear to have taken the form of 'steans', large convex-sided jars made from the local clay and fired with a glossy internal glaze.[31]

A number of tall, slightly convex cylindrical jars excavated from the late sixteenth- to early seventeenth-century potteries of the Hampshire-Surrey border have been described as butter pots. Measuring some 7½ inches in height by 3½ inches in diameter, they are amongst the smallest vessels of this type.[32]

The butter pots made in the eighteenth-century Verwood potteries in Dorset were quite large, however, their slightly conical bodies some 17½ inches in height flaring towards the rim, handles being applied at each side for ease of handling.[33] Made of the local buff-firing clay, their interiors were coated in a green-brown glaze to prevent the moisture being absorbed from the five gallons of butter they contained.

In the nineteenth and twentieth centuries in the North-country coarseware potteries, large pots were made for the storage of butter for domestic use. Most were thrown to a

**7.**
Used for preserving
butter in salt, these
pots come from:
(A-C) late
seventeenth century
North Staffordshire;
(D) the eighteenth
century Verwood
pottery in Dorset; (E)
seventeenth century
Oxford; (F) the
Weatheriggs Pottery,
Cumbria, 1960s; (G)
James Pearson's
Oldfield Pottery at
Brampton,
Derbyshire, c.1924,
in sizes from ½ to 4
gallons, and (H)
Pearson & Co.'s
Whittington Moor
Potteries, Derbyshire,
c.1940, in sizes to
hold 8 to 18 lb. The
lard-pots come from
late Victorian
Newcastle-upon-Tyne
(I) and West
Surrey (J).

tall, cylindrical form in red earthenware, their interiors
and the upper part of their exteriors usually being coated
in a black or dark brown lead glaze. The catalogue of John
Patterson, successor to Samuel Moore & Co., of Bridge

Pottery, Monkwearmouth, Sunderland, offered butter jars from five shillings to sixpence each in 1883, for example, while in 1921 Doulton's Sunderland Works was producing them from 18 inches high at 8s 6d each to 6½ inches high at tenpence each, all these being finished with white interiors. At Ambrose Walker's pottery at Thornton-on-Tees they were made from 15¾ inches high and 14 inches wide at four shillings each down to 7 inches high and 6 inches wide at sixpence each.

The stoneware potters of Derbyshire were also producing butter pots until quite recently, the 1924 catalogue of James Pearson's Oldfield Pottery at Brampton near Chesterfield having lidded pots in various sizes ranging from half-gallons at sixpence-halfpenny to four-gallons at ninepence-halfpenny each, and even larger ones at tenpence per gallon thereafter. Smaller butter jars holding from eight to eighteen pounds were made at 10s. 9d. to 22s. per dozen at Pearson's Whittington Moor Potteries throughout the 1940s, and these were probably the last to be produced in this country.

During the inter-war years the processing of milk into butter had generally ceased to be a farmhouse activity due to the emergence of large commercial creameries. Even so, a few butter pots were still to be found in the stock of a number of the traditional potters I visited in the region during the 1960s.

**Lard Pots**  The traditional way to keep lard was to melt it 'in a jar put in a kettle of water and boiled; run it into bladders that have been extremely well cleaned. The smaller they are the better the lard keeps; as, after the air reaches it, it becomes rank. Put in a sprig of rosemary when melting.'[34] By the nineteenth century a number of potteries were making purposely-designed lard pots with rounded bodies and wide mouths. Pottery vessels could easily have been used as lard-pots at earlier periods, but, having no particular characteristics, they are indistinguishable from other forms of storage jar.

The main requirements for preserve and pickling jars is that they should have totally non-absorbent interiors, wide bodies and mouths to give ready access to their contents, and a rolled rim over which a bladder or similar sealing can be tied. Tin-glazed vessels of this type, now known as *albarellos*, were used in ninth-century Persia and Syria, from where their manufacture had spread to Spain and Italy probably by the late thirteenth century. The Port Books of Southampton record the importation of these 'painted pots' by Venetian or Genoan galleys in the 1430s, thus explaining their alternative English name of 'galleypots'.

At that period, the English pottery industry was quite incapable of producing anything approaching these wares with regard to their quality, decoration, or sheer utility; but by the sixteenth century direct copies were being made in both the copper-green lead-glazed earthenwares of West Surrey and in the yellow lead-glazed earthenware of the Midlands.[35] The techniques of making tin-glazed earthenware were now spreading across Europe, however, entering Holland at the opening of the sixteenth century, from where they were brought across into England by two Antwerp potters, Jasper Andries and Jacob Jansen. Having arrived in Norwich in 1567, these two men established their factory in the London parish of Aldgate soon after 1571. From this time the London recipe books begin to take a much greater interest in preserving fruits in sugar syrups or in honey contained within 'Gallypots', presumably using the wares produced at this newly-established local source.[36] The manufacture of the milky-white tin-glazed 'delftware' or 'galleypot-ware' soon spread to the Bristol area, to Liverpool, Glasgow and Ireland, but then it went into a rapid decline as the Staffordshire potters began to introduce their greatly improved varieties of pottery in the mid-eighteenth century.

Although both delftware galleypots and their lead-glazed earthenware counterparts were very useful for preserving, they were quite unsuitable for pickling, since the vinegar solutions leached the lead out of their glazes, contaminating

**Preserve and Pickling Jars**

55

the contents and making them dangerously poisonous. A much improved form of pottery which overcame this problem had been imported into England from Germany ever since the fourteenth century. Called stoneware, it was fired to a very high temperature, some 1200–1400°C, so that its clay became completely vitrified and non-porous. Its fine 'orange-peel' glaze was achieved by throwing salt into the kiln, whereupon the vapour combined with the clay to produce a hard-wearing, insoluble and stain-resistant surface.

In 1671–2 John Dwight of Fulham began the first commercially-successful stoneware pottery in England, his agreement of 1676 with the London Glass-Sellers Company stating that his products included 'Fine pickling potts and pitchers'. There was such a great demand for these wares that by the late seventeenth century further stoneware potteries had been set up in London, Nottingham, Crich in Derbyshire, Burslem in Staffordshire, and perhaps in Bristol too. This expansion continued throughout the eighteenth and nineteenth centuries, with further potteries being established around the existing centres, as well as in Dorset, and in the neighbourhood of Liverpool, Chesterfield, Sheffield, Leeds, Bradford, Halifax, Burton-in-Lonsdale, Castleford and Newcastle-upon-Tyne.[37]

All these pottery works made a wide selection of bottles, flasks and mugs, together with many fine ornamental and commemorative wares, but much of their income was drawn from the sale of preserve and pickling jars. Some of the earliest English examples were direct copies of their delftware predecessors, their cylindrical bodies having a constriction just below the rim so that their covers could be securely tied in place across their mouths. By the second half of the eighteenth century some of these had adopted a simple cylindrical form, the constriction shrinking to a narrow U-shaped channel. With either plain or vertically-ribbed sides, they were particularly popular in the late nineteenth and early twentieth centuries, especially for

*Pots for Potting*

**8.**
Preserve and pickling jars. Ultimately derived from the 9th century *albarellos* of Persia, these English jars come from: (A) the sixteenth century green-glazed West Surrey potteries; (B) the mid seventeenth century Southwark delftware potteries; (C) Basing House, Hampshire (early seventeenth century white delftware); (D) a late seventeenth century London brown saltglaze pottery; (E) Crich brown saltglaze pottery, Derbyshire, dated April 29th, 1786; (F) Belper brown stoneware pottery, Derbyshire, dated 1799; and (G) Mortlake brown stoneware pottery, London, dated November 28th, 1752, this example being decorated with miniature inn-signs. The black-glazed red earthenware jar (H) made at Midhope Pottery, South Yorkshire, in the mid nineteenth century, was used to store yeast by burial in the garden.

packing preserves made by major manufacturers such as Crosse & Blackwell or William P. Hartley. Manufacturers such as James Pearson of Oldfield Pottery, Brampton in Derbyshire, for example, were offering plain or fluted grey stoneware jars from 1 lb at 8s 6d per gross to 4 lb at 19s per gross in their 1924 price lists.

From the mid-eighteenth century too, other jars developed a slightly taller form, with a bold rounded rim above a deep concave constriction, their square-shouldered bodies tapering slightly towards a narrow moulding around the base. For larger quantities the earlier pickle or storage jars tended to be baluster-shaped, becoming cylindrical with rounded shoulders from the mid-eighteenth century through to modern times.

During the sixteenth century, glass jars had sometimes been used for preserving and pickling, their hard, transparent material admirably showing off the contents. So long as glass was hand-made in fairly small-scale factories, its expense prohibited its widespread use. In the early to mid nineteenth century, however, the mass-production of glass vessels enabled them to compete so successfully with earthenwares and stonewares that they began to take over the market completely. After the First World War, glass jars were used for the majority of all the jams and pickles made in this country, although cylindrical stoneware jars survived for the packaging of top-quality marmalade as a food-gift until quite recently.

***Egg Preserving Jars***  Up to the early nineteenth century most eggs were preserved by being cleaned and then either coated with an air-tight solution of gum arabic, or smeared with butter or sweet oil, after which they were packed in bran or sawdust.[38] It was then found that they could also be kept for up to two years by being immersed in a lime-water solution:

EGGS: To Keep
Pour a full gallon of boiling water on two quarts of quicklime and ½ lb salt. When cold mix into it 1 oz of cream of tartar, and the day following put in the

eggs. After the lime has been stirred well into the boiling water a large part of it will settle at the bottom of the vessel, on which the eggs will remain.[39]

As alternatives, solutions of water-glass (silicate of soda) or isinglass (a form of gelatine derived from freshwater fish) were used for the same purpose in most households up to the 1950s or early 1960s, when the increasing availability of eggs from battery-hens made the home preservation of eggs quite unnecessary.

Any large waterproof jar could be used for this purpose, but some manufacturers, such as James Pearson of Oldfield Pottery, Brampton, near Chesterfield, made special cylindrical open-topped egg-preserving pans in glazed stoneware. Their price lists of the 1940s include one- to six-gallon pans at 1s 3d to 7s 6d each, lids extra, estimating that they would hold approximately fifty eggs to the gallon.

**Pots for Preservation by Burial**

It was in the 1930s that the late Professor Gerhard Bersu first suggested that some of the large pits found on Iron Age sites were not subterranean homes after all, but actually functioned as efficient grain stores. Since that time, practical experiments have confirmed his views. Once the pit had been filled it was sealed with a moist clay or dung plug and finally covered with a layer of earth to provide insulation and to prevent it from drying out. The grain then respired converting the oxygen in the trapped air into sufficient carbon dioxide (up to 30%) to prevent further decomposition, so long as the temperature did not rise above twelve degrees Celsius.[40]

Similar principles were certainly being used for a variety of foodstuffs in the post-medieval period, as illustrated in the following instructions given by Mrs Elizabeth Moxon of Pontefract in her *English Housewifery Exemplified* published in Leeds in 1741:

To preserve Fruit Green all the Year
Gather your Fruit when they are three Parts
Ripe, on a very dry Day, when the Sun shines on
them, then take Earthen Pots and put them in, cover
the Pots with Cork, or bung them that no air can get
into them, dig a Place in the Earth a Yard deep, set
the Pots therein, and cover them with Earth very
close, and keep them for use; when you take them
out cover 'em as at first.

In the same way, liquid yeast for home brewing was preserved from one brew to the next by being poured into a jar, which was then sealed with a cloth and buried in the garden. A dark brown-glazed jar in the Sheffield City Museum collection was formerly used for this purpose in the Midhope area of South Yorkshire.[41] Strong home-brewed ale was also buried in the ground to facilitate a long, slow maturing. Ammon Wrigley has recorded how the 'sheep-washing ale' made by the shepherds of the Saddleworth Moors of the West Riding of Yorkshire used to be buried in the peat ready for the washing-day. Four gallons of ale prepared for haytime probably lies within Woodward Hill to this day, since its owners never re-discovered its whereabouts, even after prolonged searching.[42]

Rather more up-market, Richard Bradley advised that miniature cellars for storing bottles of ale or wine could be made by sinking large oil jars into holes in the ground with 'the Earth filled close about the sides; One of these Jars may hold about a dozen quart Bottles, and will keep the Drink very well; but the tops of the Jars must be kept close cover'd up'.[43] In a similar manner, Sir Hugh Platt informs us that hazel nuts could be stored 'in earthen pottes well stopt a foote or two in the ground: they keep best in gravellie or sandy places . . .'.[44] Virtually any pottery vessel could be used in this method of preservation, so long as it had a mouth which could be securely sealed to prevent the circulation of air around its contents.

It is quite probable that pottery vessels have been used for the storage of dry foodstuffs from the medieval period at least, their convenient size, their insect and rodent-proof materials, the ease with which they could be sealed, and, in some cases, their capability of being stacked one upon another, making them ideal for this purpose. It was not until the late nineteenth or early twentieth century, however, that museums began to record the usages to which the pottery they collected had actually been put. The Hampshire County Museums Service, for example, has a fine large bulbous jar dated 1774, its practical purpose being quite unintelligible, were it not that the collector had noted that it was used for storing nuts at a farm in the Franham area.

**Pots for Dry Storage**

### Bread Pots

In the early nineteenth century, large pottery vessels were used for the storage of loaves of bread, their glazed interiors and ceramic lids ensuring that their contents did not go stale. Their shapes varied considerably from one area of the country to another. In general terms, however, those of the lowland zone, approximately south of a line running from the Bristol Channel to the Wash, are lidded versions of the broad pans made for washing and other general household purposes in this region. To the north, they are much taller, usually having a baluster-shaped form, although straight- and conical-sided versions are also known. The lids made throughout the south, and also in the north-east of England, tended to be flat-topped, with sharp-shouldered conical sides descending to a broad rim. Those of Wales were tall domes, topped with circular knobs, while in the north Midlands, Yorkshire, and the north-west of the country, flat lids with integrally-thrown doughnut-shaped knobs predominated. Stoneware bread-pots usually had quite different shapes, cylindrical pots with flat or domed lids being the most common, although some manufacturers, such as Doultons of Lambeth, made their own unique designs.

**9.**
Bread pots. These Victorian pots, all but (H) being made in lead-glazed earthenware, come from: (A) & (B) Weatheriggs Pottery, Cumbria; (C) & (D) Scott's Pottery, Sunderland, c.1880; (E) probably one of the Newcastle-upon-Tyne potteries; (F) one of the Halifax potteries; (G) Oxfordshire; (H) the Royal Doulton (stoneware) potteries, Lambeth; (I) Wrecclesham Pottery, Farnham, Surrey; (J) Verwood Pottery, Dorset; (K) Helston, Cornwall; (L) Ewenny Pottery, South Wales, and (M) the Buckley potteries, North Wales.

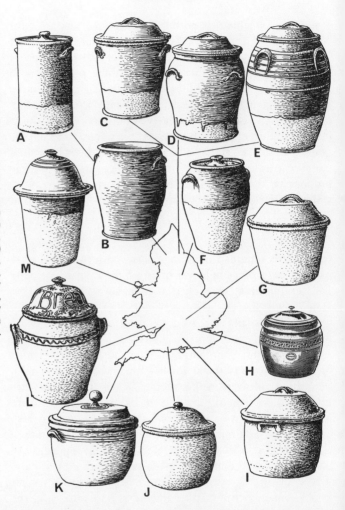

*Storage Jars*

From the late Victorian period, a number of potteries began to produce sets of lidded earthenware jars for the storage of dry foods such as rice, oatmeal, peas, cornflour, etc, the title of their contents being printed or impressed

62

around their cylindrical bodies. Since that time they have remained in production, their designs keeping pace with current fashions in domestic style. From around the 1920s to the 1960s, for example, the broad blue-and-white slip-banded 'Cornish Wares', made in Castleford, Stoke-on-Trent, and other potteries, were perhaps the most popular. These were succeeded by jars with screen-printed designs and coloured glazes influenced by contemporary studio pottery, their lids perhaps being of teak fitted with a plastic sealing-strip. To this range, attractive transfer-printed designs have now been added.

Stoneware storage jars have also remained in use, their traditional forms sometimes being enriched with muted glazes when produced by the studio potters fashionable from the 1960s. Since then, simple, functional brown salt-glazed stoneware jars in the French tradition have been widely sold in this country, their mouths often being sealed with large corks to present a particularly 'rustic' appearance.

It was five hundred years ago that the potters began to take over the national market for preserving-vessels, a market they were to dominate for four and a half centuries. During that period they enabled people of all classes to preserve a variety of foods in times of relative plenty, ready for times of scarcity, such as the bleak winter months, thus greatly improving the overall quality of life. A great technical innovation in their own time, the pottery vessels were in turn superseded by new innovations in food technology, ranging from canning and freeze-drying to vacuum-packing and deep-freezing. Largely deprived of their functional role, those preserving pots which remain in use today are mainly appreciated for their aesthetic qualities, especially when combined with fine foods to form high quality food-gifts for special occasions. As to the potteries whose livelihoods depended on the manufacture of preserving pots of all kinds, they were, for the most part, liquidated in the years following the First World War, those few which remained having to diversify into horticultural wares, into tourist pottery, or into those wares which could be sold through fashionable kitchen shops set up in London and the major provincial towns.

**Notes and References**

1. OED, *s.v.* 'Potting'.
2. A. Boorde, *A Compendyous Regyment, or A Dyetary of Helth*, 1542, ed. F. J. Furnivall (Early English Text Society, ES 10, 1870), p. 274; G. Emmison, *Tudor Food & Pastimes* (London, 1964), p. 47; F. Peel, *The Spen Valley Past & Present* (Heckmondwike, 1893), p. 93; R. Warner, *Antiquitates Culinariae* (London, 1791), p. 94.
3. R. Bradley, *The Country Housewife and Lady's Director*, pt. 2 (1732, reprinted London, 1980), p. 84.
4. C. B. Hieatt & S. Butler, eds., *Curye on Inglysch* (Early English Text Society, SS 8, 1985), p. 88.
5. W. E. Mead, *The English Medieval Feast* (London, 1931), pp. 95–6.
6. Sir K. Digby, *The Closet of Sir Kenelm Digby Opened* (1669, reprinted London, 1910), p. 184.
7. A. Davidson, *North Atlantic Seafood* (London, 1980), pp. 450–1.
8. P. Brears, *Traditional Food in Yorkshire* (Edinburgh, 1987), pp. 178–9.
9. Hieatt & Butler, pp. 124; 141; 178.
10. Digby, p. 185.
11. W.M., *The Compleat Cook* (London, 1655), p. 115.
12. Leeds University, Brotherton Library, Bedford MSS 432/4, pp. 39–40.
13. J. Fell, 'Some illustrations of home life in Lonsdale', *Cumberland & Westmorland Archaeological and Antiquarian Society, Trans.*, 11 (1891), p. 387.
14. ibid., p. 397.
15. B. Bloice, 'Norfolk House, Lambeth', *Post-Medieval Archaeology* 5 (1972), pp. 127–8.
16. E. Gooder, 'The finds from the cellar of the Old Hall, Temple Balsall, Warwickshire', *Post-Medieval Archaeology*, 18 (1984), p. 175.
17. H. Glasse, *The Art of Cookery Made Plain and Easy* (London, 1747), p. 117.
18. D. Hartley, *Food in England* (London, 1954), p. 281.
19. R. C. Bell, *Tyneside Pottery* (London, 1971), p. 68.
20. C. A. Wilson, *Food and Drink in Britain* (Harmondsworth, Penguin, 1976), p. 21.
21. Rebecca Price, *The Compleat Cook*, ed. M. Masson (London, 1974), p. 99; P. Mayes, 'A seventeenth-century kiln site at Pettersbury, Northants', *Post-Medieval Archaeology* 2 (1968), p. 59.
22. J. M. Baines, *Sussex Pottery* (Brighton, 1980), pp. 64; 185; and original catalogues in the collection of the North of England Open Air Museum, Beamish, County Durham.

23. ibid.
24. Hartley, p. 332.
25. M. Dunn, 'Remarks on some Cornish fishes', *Royal Institution of Cornwall, Journal* 6 (1878–81), p. 357.
26. Glasse, p. 156.
27. J. M. Wilson, *The Farmer's Dictionary* (Edinburgh, n.d.), p. 252.
28. L. Weatherill, *The Pottery Trade and North Staffordshire, 1660–1760* (Manchester, 1971), p. 77.
29. F. Redfern, *History of the Town of Uttoxeter* (London, 1865), p. 274.
30. A. Grant, *North Devon Pottery: the Seventeenth Century* (Exeter, 1983), p. 54.
31. ibid., pp. 104; 120; 126.
32. F. W. Hollings, 'A preliminary note on the pottery industry of the Hants.–Surrey border', *Surrey Archaeological Collections* 68 (1971), pp. 77–8.
33. D. Algar, A. Light & P. Trehane, *The Verwood & District Potteries* (Ringwood, 1979), p. 15.
34. A. Heath, *Pig Curing & Cooking* (London, 1952), p. 25.
35. L. Matthews, 'Green-glazed English Albarellos', *Post-Medieval Archaeology* 6 (1972), pp. 202–6; P. C. D. Brears, *Catalogue of English Country Pottery at the Yorkshire Museum, York* (York, 1968), p. 11: P. Mayes & L. A. S. Butler, *Sandal Castle Excavations* (Wakefield, 1983), p. 222.
36. See, e.g., T. Dawson, *The Good Huswife's Jewell* (London, 1596), p. 38; *The Second Part of the Good Hus-wives Iewell* (London, 1597), p. 72.
37. See: A. Oswald, R. J. C. Hildyard & R. G. Hughes, *English Brown Stoneware 1670–1900* (London, 1982) for information on this type of pottery.
38. E. Acton, *Modern Cookery for Private Families* (London, 1855), p. 444; I. Beeton, *The Book of Household Management* (London, 1861), p. 823.
39. Beeton, p. 823: *The Book of the Household* (London, C. 1860), p. 459.
40. P. Reynolds, 'Pit technology in the Iron Age', *British Archaeology*, 10 (1988), pp. 24–6.
41. Sheffield City Museums, K 1921–58.
42. A. Wrigley, *Old Saddleworth Days* (Oldham, 1920), p. 268.
43. R. Bradley, *The Country Housewife and Lady's Director*, pt. 1, 6th ed (1736, reprinted London, 1980), p. 54.
44. Sir Hugh Platt, *Delightes for Ladies* (London, 1605), A72.

# 4.

## *Necessities and Luxuries: Food Preservation from the Elizabethan to the Georgian Era*

JENNIFER STEAD

The sixteenth century saw a spectacular increase of activity in food preservation. The need to victual ships which made long voyages of exploration, taking months and even years, spurred the European maritime nations into experimenting with preserving foods which would ensure the health and lives of their seamen. This, together with the new exotic fruits and vegetables brought back to Europe, and above all, the increased supply of sugar from Caribbean islands and North Africa resulted in a veritable explosion of new methods. The sixteenth-century housewife benefitted from these discoveries no less than her twentieth-century counterpart did from the exploration of outer space, which introduced new cookware and new long-life convenience foods. However, all through the period from the sixteenth to the nineteenth century it was the better-off who benefitted, and the rich most of all. Mariners' food did not improve. British working people continued to eat subsistence foods: mainly peas, beans, oatmeal or other cereal, bacon, salt meat and salt fish, eked out by vegetables, herbs and hedgerow nuts and fruits in season, a little cheese, with fresh meat when they could afford it or catch it wild, or when they killed their own pig or poultry. The well-off ate large amounts of fresh food in season; they also consumed a great variety of preserved foods made by both old and new methods which were luxuries, such as hams, potted and soused meats and fish, pickles of all kinds, preserved and dried fruits and sweetmeats, and preserved vegetables including peas, artichokes and asparagus.

Improved winter foddering of animals in lowland Britain meant that fresh meat was always available to those who could afford it, even in the sixteenth century. In Scotland the diet books of St Andrews University in the 1580s show that beef, both salt and fresh, was the mainstay of the students' diet, and that fresh beef was available all winter.[1] The greatest number of preserving recipes in English cookery books of the seventeenth and eighteenth centuries were for meat and fish, and these were perfected to a high art, certain regions winning renown for the quality of their cured and salted meats and fish. Even today, smoked salmon, salt beef silversides and briskets, gammons and hams make English feast foods superb, while our everyday dishes are undistinguished and even poor.[2] Although French and other Continental fruit and vegetable preserves far exceeded ours in variety and excellence, the English preserved meats were better than the French: 'In ffraunce, the people salten but lytill mete, except their bacon'.[3] However, Continental large-grained Bay salt (evaporated from seawater on the beaches of the Bay of Bourgneuf, and all along the Atlantic coast of France and northern Spain and Portugal) was preferred by the English to most native salt, which was too fine for preserving purposes. Fine salt is not so good for curing because it leaches out liquids faster than the salt can seep in; it has the effect of sealing the surface and the salt cannot penetrate. But large-grained salt is slow dissolving, and will penetrate.[4] In the eighteenth century, Lounds's salt from Nantwich in Cheshire was considered among the best of English salt for preserving meat, and Hannah Glasse (1747) said that York hams were famous because they were cured with Maldon salt brought from Essex: 'it is a large clear Salt, and gives the

**Salting and Smoking**

67

Meat a fine Flavour'. She thought Maldon salt was also the best for potting butter. Suffolk butter preserved with it was very good.[5]

Salt preserves foods by arresting bacterial growth at solutions of twenty-five per cent or more. A weaker solution inhibits many other bacteria, but there are organisms which thrive in a saline solution, although at extremely high strengths all organic and enzyme action is stopped. Salt draws out the liquid from foods by osmosis, thus preventing organisms from obtaining moisture in which to grow. Saltpetre, however, actually kills bacteria. It was observed in the seventeenth century that salt was not necessary for preserving as saltpetre alone (the main constituent of gunpowder) would preserve.[6] This new preservative had been discovered when it was found that gunpowder rubbed into hanging game enhanced its keeping qualities. Saltpetre or 'nitre' is a nitrate of potassium or sodium. Petre salt was nitre in its native state; when refined it was saltpetre. Salprunella was made by melting nitre in a crucible, then repeatedly throwing on charcoal dust whereupon the violent reactions converted some of the potassium nitrate into nitrites, which started the curing faster.[7] Nitrites react with blood to preserve a red colour. Just ¼–½ oz of salprunella is enough for 100 lbs of meat; any more makes meat dark and hard, while the pickle goes green. Too much is dangerous to health; nitrite poisoning turns one blue, widens blood vessels causing headaches and can cause cancer.

However, many recipes stipulated dangerous amounts of salprunella and saltpetre. As Ann Cook pointed out, Hannah Glasse's recipe 'To Pot Beef like Venison' contained 'salts sufficient to colour a whole Beef red'. The recipe required, to only 8 lbs of beef, 1 oz salprunella, 4 oz salt-petre, 4 oz peter-salt and a pint of coarse salt.[8] Some people refused to use salprunella at all, saying it 'eats out the Gravey and Goodness of the Meat, makes it unpleasantly dry, and gives it an unsavoury Twang'.[9] Too much salt meat in the diet was not considered healthy. It was thought to cause the stone, scurvy and leprosy;[10] it was 'hard of dygestion' and produced constant thirst. It is now known that excess salt can exacerbate high blood pressure, and that infants have difficulty in excreting it efficiently because of their immature kidneys.

The salt taxes imposed from 1643 and not repealed until 1825 may have been an important factor in the decline of the popularity of salt foods. The salt herring industry was hit immediately. However, fashions were already changing in the sixteenth century; hard dry salt fish began to be despised in Elizabeth's day, although in Catholic countries it has continued to be eaten until the present. The social position of salt hake can be inferred from its name, Poor John.[11] After the Restoration dried salt fish became widely unpopular as better preservative methods appeared, and it was relegated to the diet of the poor, the army and navy, but wet salt fish, such as herring, salmon, oysters and anchovies remained acceptable foods. Nevertheless, even these were not in great demand, as can be seen in a 1688 list of almost forty fish dishes for Lent, only one of which is salt: salt eels.[12] Dried salt cod with parsnips and egg sauce was a Lenten dish which survived, especially among Catholics until the twentieth century. The Reverend J. G. Wood wrote in 1863, 'Salt cod is to many persons a great dainty, but to others, among whom I must be reckoned, it is unsufferably offensive, and even with all the additions of sauce and condiment is barely eatable.'[13] Ling was considered the best of salt fish: 'Ling perhaps looks for great extolling, being counted beefe of the sea, and standing every fish day (as a cold supporter) at my Lord Mayor's table; yet it is nothing but long Cod. When it is salted it is called Ling . . . the longer it lyeth . . . the better it is waxing in the end as yellow as a gold noble.'[14] Ling, like haberden (cod or haddock) was prepared in two forms: salted ('Old Ling') or simply air-dried like stockfish and buckthorn (whiting).[15] Catholic Ireland and parts of Scotland were reputed to cook air-dried ling to perfection in buttermilk.[16] Tusser wrote that salt fish was best bought after harvest, when it was cheapest, and kept for five or six months for Lent. It had to be kept very dry:

> Choose skilfully salt-fish . . .
> . . . and go stack it up dry,
> With pease-straw between it, the safer to lie.[17]

Dried salt fish kept better than wet-salted fish. Salted herrings were packed tightly in barrels of brine to exclude air, and when this was done correctly they kept for a year.[18] But Tusser advised:

> Spend herring first, save salt fish last
> For salt-fish is good, when Lent is past.

In the fifteenth century there had been more salt fish than fresh, with a huge demand for fish both salt and fresh during Lent.[19] Aberdeen salmon, salted and smoked, was exported to the Continent in the thirteenth century; by the seventeenth century the trade amounted to 170 tons annually. These salmon were hard, dry and very salty. A recipe of 1584 shows that salt salmon was minced and served with a sauce of mustard, vinegar and sugar.[20] Oysters could be kept alive in brine for twelve days,[21] and for two weeks in cold weather, the brine being changed every twenty-four hours. Anchovies pickled in brine were imported from the Continent in Elizabeth's time, but mock anchovies were made of sprats or smelts.[22]

Salt was used to preserve suet. Great quantities of suet were needed by farmers at harvest time to make pies and puddings for the hired hands, and William Ellis commended the practice of farmers' wives who, throughout the year, collected the raw fat and suet off beef, chopped it very small, mixed it with plenty of salt and pepper and pressed it down hard in pots so that no air remained, then covered it close and kept it in a cool dry place. Kept any other way, 'it would surely stink in a little time'. Even raw sausage-meat could be kept thus.[23] Besides salt, the essential oils in the pepper acted as a preservative.

Pork was the most commonly salted meat, but mutton could be made into 'hams', and beef, fowls and geese were also salted and dried or smoked. Martilmas beef or hung beef was usually prepared between November 11th (Martinmas) and Christmas. It was a useful addition to the diet in winter, especially for those living far away from sources of fresh meat. It was also called Dutch Beef. Nathan Bailey (1736) gave an explanation for the name when he wrote that in September in Holland, cows and heifers were killed, cut in family-sized pieces, and put in a brine composed of five handfuls of common salt, three handfuls of Bay salt, a handful each of rock petre and petre salt boiled in pump water so the brine would be heavy enough to float an egg, with the addition of half a pint of vinegar. This drew out the bloody juices which would otherwise putrefy. The raw meat was then taken out, and salted well with Bay salt, rock salt, petre salt and petre for ten to fourteen days, then rolled up, and wrapped in three or four sheets of brown paper to protect it from the ill flavour of coal smoke, and hung in the chimney to dry (but not where it was too warm).[24] William Ellis, writing in 1750, said that Dutch or hung beef was made best in the North: 'we in the Southern Parts of *England* do not prepare hung Beef so well as they do in *Lancashire* and the North; because they dry it there with the smoak of Turf, which gives the Beef such a very pleasant tang, that it is much coveted and sent for to considerable Distances'.[25] Richard Bradley said 'It is, in my opinion, better than any Bacon to be boiled and eaten hot'.[26] Ellis wrote that in Scotland in the 1720s, 'there is hardly any such thing as mutton to be had till August, or beef till September; that is to say, in quality fit to be eaten; and both go out about Christmas. And therefore at or about Martinmas such of the

71

inhabitants who are anything beforehand with the world, salt up a quantity of beef, as if they were going on a voyage.'[27] Up to the mid-nineteenth century West Riding clothiers and better working class households would buy a whole beef among several families at Martinmas, and share it out to make hung beef. It was hung from joists on big hooks or in a ventilated cupboard (aumbry) or kept buried in oatmeal, oatchaff or wheatstraw.[28] Hung beef was very useful, but the lack of gravy was a drawback. Ann Cook wrote (1754) of the predicament of country dwellers who did not live near a market:

> In Town I made my Market every Day, the Butchers Meat so fresh and sweet that my Beef-gravy made Sauces, and Soops delicious: But here we kill a Beef once a Month, and that alters the Case, for I can have fresh Beef one week in the whole Month; so there is three Weeks of the Month I have no Beef-soop nor Beef-gravy for Sauces, without sending to the market for fresh beef.[29]

When wanted for use, salt beef had to be boiled a long time with hay or bran to get rid of the salt, or boiled in pottages with plenty of herbs or vegetables. Salt beef for the navy was not hung and dried, but left in salt, sometimes for five or six years so that it was practically inedible, and many ideas were put forward for preserving meat unsalted.[30] The problem was not solved until meat was canned in the early nineteenth century.

The most important and useful animal for preserving was the pig, and bacon was the most popular way of preserving it. Ellis wrote (1750):

> Bacon is a serviceable, palatable, profitable, and clean meat, for a ready Use in a Country house; Ready I say, because it requires not to be kept in a Cellar, or at any Distance from a Kitchen or

Chamber, but may be had at all Times of the Year
for being cut to broil, fry, boil, or bake; and if it is
not in the House, it is ready at the next Chandler's
Shop. For bacon is so universally traded in, that it
may be had at almost any Part of the kingdom; and
so serviceable to both Rich and Poor, that it saves
much Expence in Firing, time, and Trouble . . .
Where there is Bread and Bacon enough, there is no
Want . . . In the Northern Parts of *England*,
thousands of families eat little other Meat than
Bacon; and indeed, in the Southern parts, more than
ever live on Bacon, or Pickled Pork, or on both,
since trade has lessened, and the Number of
Families increased.

Pigs intended for bacon were fattened to huge proportions
of fifty or sixty Smithfield stones (of 8 lbs to the stone) 'for
we cannot have too fat nor too large a Flitch'.[31] Pigs were
bred so fat because the fat took salt well and yet tasted
mildly of it, whereas lean flesh took it up much more
readily and often tasted far too salty. A heavy fat
consumption suited the constitution of those people with
heavy outdoor occupations. It was important to kill the pig
intended for bacon or ham in cold weather: Allhollantide
(October 31) to Lady Day (March 25) was the period for
killing. The pigs in a neighbourhood were killed at intervals
so that the perishable offal could be shared among
neighbours every few weeks, rather than all at once in a
November glut. For bacon and ham it was considered
important that the pigs should not be chased or frightened.
(The modern explanation is that a well-rested pig has
plenty of glycogen in the muscles, which, when it is killed,
turns to lactic acid and this opens up muscle fibre and
allows salts to penetrate more quickly; also the lactic acid
inhibits bacterial growth.)

The pig would have less chance to be frightened if it
were killed in its own familiar surroundings, being stunned

73

and bled first for ten minutes or so until the heart had pumped all the blood out. The blood was made immediately into black puddings. The bled pig was scalded to soften the hairs, and the hairs were scraped or singed off (some considered singeing gave the fat a bad taste). An innovation in the seventeenth century was to inject brine directly into the femoral artery. Syringes were made 'at 2 or 3 places in London'.[32] Bladders fitted with a pipe used in medicine as clysters or enemas were also used, but these were apt to break or spill, and syringes exerted more force. The injecting of brine was then largely forgotten until the twentieth century.[33]

The pig was cut up and boned, rubbed with salt to fetch out the bloody juice and allowed to drain for twenty-four hours. Then 4 oz saltpetre (and sometimes salprunella) to a 60-stone hog was rubbed in; then a peck more of common salt, usually mixed with Bay salt and sometimes brown sugar, was rubbed in and heaped on, and the salted pieces were stacked and turned for ten to twelve days. Then 'we hang them up in our wide Country Chimney Corners to dry for a Week or two, or three'; the flitches were not to get in the least warm or they would rust or spoil. When the bacon was made in March or April, it was left only three days in the chimney corner, then laid on a rack hung under the kitchen ceiling to dry leisurely. Ellis preferred this plain dried bacon to smoked bacon which had 'that nasty, unwholesome, unpleasant Smoak Twang'.[34] Bacon could be kept sweet and sound in a heap of clean wheatstraw that had been dried in the oven, or in a heap of dried brown malt, or rolled in bran or fine wood ashes.

Commercial curers killed at any time, since the meat was cured and sold quickly. Drying in the great smoke room was quick: hogs were turned into bacon in only four to six weeks.[35] Some London bacon manufacturers produced bacon in as little as eight days, but it tainted quickly and was taken to country markets to sell cheaply to poor people.[36] Sliced bacon collops were a peculiarly British cut, and fried bacon and eggs a peculiarly British dish. On the Continent bacon was used largely in stews. The poor in Britain ate bacon and pease pottage or bean pottage until Lent, when the bacon was put away until after Easter.[37]

Smoke was often objected to on the grounds that it was deleterious to both flavour and health. Turf smoke was the least objectionable. Smoke, in drying out meats, adds formaldehyde, alcohols, tars, creosotes, phenols and other chemicals. Sausages were seldom smoked in England. There was no need to make a variety of dried sausages as, for instance, were made in north-west Germany where fresh meat was only eaten on the four killing days in each year. The British were amply supplied with, and preferred, fresh meat and fresh sausages, and so, apart from black and white puddings and haggis, a single British sausage stands out as popular from the seventeenth century: this was Polony, or Bologna sausage. A 1688 definition runs: 'Bolonia sausages, these are only made in *September*, they are Beef Guts filled with minced Pork and stampt: to which mixt Pepper, Cloves, Nutmegs, Salt, and Salt-peter, Caraway seeds, and Cinnamon: tied about a Finger long.'[38] These were coloured pink, with red sage at first, then saltpetre was used instead. Smoked for three or four days, and hung in a dry place for six weeks, oiled and stored in a box of wood ashes, they would keep for months. William Rabisha wrote (1661): 'and when you will used them, they must be cut out very thin round ways, and put them in your dish with oil and vinegar, and serve them for a salad for the second course.'[39]

The buttocks and legs of pigs were made into hams. Hams, and other meats, could be cured in a strong pickle of sugar, salt and saltpetre for three weeks to two months, then hung to dry. Yorkshire hams sold in London for 5d a pound in the early eighteenth century.[40] Bradley described the smoking-house at Canterbury designed for sixty large hogs at a time, and observed that English smoking was very casual compared with German. The English used more salt and less smoke; the Germans used less salt and no saltpetre, but more smoke, in very ingeniously designed smoke closets.[41] Saltpetre's hardening and colouring properties Ellis considered very proper for ham, but sugar was also good, because it counteracted the hardening, and 'makes the Flesh eat tender, short, and sweet'. Honey had been used from Roman times in the cure; honey and sugar remove moisture by osmosis in the same way as salt, and the sweet cure was for centuries considered essential, but is rarely used today. Brown sugar was sometimes used alone first for two to three days.[42] Westphalia ham was much admired; it had originally been made from bear or bear cub. English imitations were flavoured with strong aromatic herbs and boiled with oak sawdust to make them red.[43] Hannah Glasse stipulated that if one wanted to keep hams a long time, then one should 'hang them a Month or two in a damp Place, so as they will be mouldy, and it will make them cut fine and short'.[44] Blue-green penicillin mould improves a ham, and it may be that Mrs Glasse was referring to this. In china-clay districts the finished hams were covered in muslin then given several layers of whitewash and hung in a dark place.[45] Elsewhere they were kept buried in oatmeal, oat hulls or wood ashes in a large box or chest. Mutton legs were cured like hams. To eat, these were not so good if boiled, but they tasted well enough cut in rashers and broiled.[46] Veal hams were also made,[47] and the same process applied to geese: 'In Holland they slit Geese down the Back, and salt them with Salt-Petre, and other Salt, and then dry them like bacon; they eat very well, if they are boiled tender.'[48] The smoked Solan geese, fashionable in Scotland in the seventeenth and eighteenth centuries, were in fact gannets from the Bass Rock or Ailsa Craig.[49]

**Pickling and Sousing: Meat and Fish**    Ham was a luxury food, and many farmers and smallholders who produced it could not afford to eat it themselves. Because of salt taxes, they had to sell the hams they made in order to buy enough salt to cure their own bacon, or to make pickled pork. Pickled pork was salted like bacon, but instead of being dried or smoked, was left to keep in the wet brine; it was sometimes called green bacon.[50] Ellis deemed pickled pork to be even better than bacon because there was no waste; bacon was apt to go rusty or be attacked by hopper-fly. Pickled pork was an admirable convenience food because, like bacon, it was instant, cheap, and available all year round. Ellis described its preparation in detail as practised by the farmers and housewives of his acquaintance: 'The pickling of pork . . . was first practised to the greatest Perfection in . . . *Kent* . . . since which the *Suffolk* Farmer has fell into such an Approbation of it, that he refuses to make Bacon.' Pork could be pickled with salt only, without saltpetre, but some folk liked the pink colour the latter gave, and its better preserving qualities. For a large porker of 36 stones [20 modern stones] 1½ lbs of coarse sugar (if used), a peck of common salt and 4 oz saltpetre were sufficient. These were rubbed carefully over the pieces which were then packed very tightly in a glazed earthenware pot, or in a salting tub, with salt piled thickly above, and a wooden cover laid on top. After twelve to fourteen days the salt had all turned to brine. Every four weeks in winter and every two weeks in summer the brine was boiled up, and added again when cold to the meat, together with fresh salt. The pieces of meat were kept down under the brine by a board and a weight. In this way the meat would keep for anything up to a year.[51] It was important to take pieces from the top first and not to meddle with pieces underneath, and never to pull them out with the fingers.[52]

Pickled pork was declared delicious, especially when boiled with lean meats in stews; it was extremely fatty, and ate 'like marrow', melting in the mouth. In Hertfordshire it was also made into pancakes by being sliced thin and dipped into batter and fried. Ellis wrote:

it is less cloying, and keeps sweet and sound longer
than any other meat whatsoever: Witness the
Approbation it meets with in the County of *Kent*,
where pickled Pork is in such general Esteem, that
they make very little Bacon there, because a Dish of
pickled Pork, with Apple Dumplins, etc is there
deemed an agreeable Repast, from the Peer to the
Peasant . . . for here the Common Plowman thinks
himself not rightly provided, if he cannot carry a
Piece of pickled Pork and Apple-Dumplin into the
Field, to bite on till he comes home to Dinner.

It was especially useful to pickle pork at harvest-time
(August) notwithstanding the hot weather for, if done
properly, it helped to feed the large numbers of harvest
workers quite cheaply.[53] A sloppier method of pickling
pork was that used for the navy. The pork was simply
thrown into barrels of brine without prior removal of
lymph and blood, which created bad flavours, and was so
salty it blistered the tongue. It was called 'barrel-pork' or
'sea-junk'.

A short-term method of keeping meat or fish was to
cook it, and then lay it in a 'sousing-drink' of salted water
with the addition of bran or oatmeal or brewers' grains or
whey. It was an excellent way of keeping pigs' offal, which
otherwise had to be eaten immediately, or given away.[54]
Meat would keep for up to a month in winter. The better-
off people enjoyed brawn prepared from a pork flitch cooked
and soused. Pigs intended for brawn were stuck with a
knife or baited with dogs so they would die slowly, which
was thought to tenderise the meat.

The flitch was boned, salted and rolled up very tightly
with cloth or tape, which required two strong men and up
to 100 yards of tape.[55] The brawn had to be boiled softly in
a huge pot over the fire or in the oven for ten to twelve
hours until so soft a straw would pass through it. When
taken out it had shrunk and the tapes had to be tied tighter,

a tricky operation; then the cold brawn was put into a souse drink. Both the boiling liquor and the souse-drink could include beer or oat-flour, milk or whey, to help keep the brawn white. Every three weeks the souse drink was changed or renewed with one or two handfuls of salt to every gallon of water. The brawn could be taken out of its drink and potted in butter.[56] Brawn was a very English dish: William Harrison's *Description* tells us that brawn with mustard was the first dish at the noon-day dinner in winter [November to February], and it was a favourite Christmas dish. Robert May (1665) described the very elaborate decoration and presentation of it. It was cut in thin slices and eaten with a mixture of pepper, salt, vinegar and oil, or lemon, or mustard.[57] Brawn remained a traditional Christmas dish until the late eighteenth century. In around 1730 it cost 12d a lb, when fresh meat was only 2d to 4d a pound. However, Bradley declared brawn was not worth the great trouble, being 'an insipid kind of Meat', an opinion shared by Ellis.[58] In the eighteenth century, its quality and popularity declined as inferior cuts such as belly and head were used, both for home-made brawn and that sold at the butchers; and it eventually ceased to be a Christmas dish.[59]

The addition of some acid to the sousing-drink prevented the proliferation of bacteria, and foods thus treated were found to keep longer. Foods kept in an acid solution were described as marinated, soused, or pickled, and collared meats and fish were treated in any of these ways. (Cooked beef pickled in vinegar had been one of the culinary 'secrets' revealed by Sir Hugh Platt in 1605.) The collaring of meats and fish, like that of brawn, simply involved boning and rolling the flesh tightly in a cloth and tying with tape before baking or boiling, to preserve a circular shape. The cooked, well-drained collars were then covered in cold souse, usually with the addition of wine or vinegar. It was important to extract all the juices or the collars would go 'foetid'.[60] Entire half-pigs boned and rolled, were made into massive collars, boiled till very tender, then kept in an acid sousing drink for as long as six months.[61] Soused foods had to be inspected regularly: 'If the pickle begins to spoil, strain it through a coarse Cloth, boil it, and skim it; when cold, pour it over. Observe, before you strain the Pickle, to wash the Collar, and wipe it dry, and wipe the Pan clean. Strain it again after it is boiled, and cover it very close'.[62] The well-off ate soused foods as side dishes in the second course at dinner, often embellished with decorative cuts stuffed with chopped herbs and spiced breadcrumbs. Collared beef was 'cut in thin Slices, and eaten with vinegar, as are most of the Collar'd-meats and Potted meats',[63] or put into a 'grand sallet'.[64] Fowls and smaller pieces of meat were pickled, and fatty fowls took the treatment better than lean, though sparrows, larks and squab-pigeons were also treated thus, the liquor boiled up once a month, until the bones were softened by the acid when the birds were served in china saucers with pickles.[65] Pigs' trotters and ears were preserved in a spiced Rhenish wine pickle, and ox palates in a wine and vinegar one. White wine was used for pale meats, and claret for beef.[66] Collared pickled beef could be dried and hung in a net.[67] The acid solution was even applied to raw meat intended for long keeping. In the Appendix to the 1758 edition of Glasse's *The Art of Cookery* there is a recipe called 'The Jews way to pickle Beef, which will go good to the West-Indies, and keep a Year good in the Pickle, and with care, will go to the East-Indies'. The raw beef was salted for seven to ten days, then covered in vinegar, with oil floated on top, and barrelled up. There is a similar recipe for raw tripe to go to the East Indies.[68]

Collared fish kept good even longer if it was drained and potted in clarified butter.[69] Most fish and seafood including sturgeon, carp, trout, anchovies, herring, mackerel, lobster, oysters etc. was simply boiled and pickled, without being rolled in collars. Flukes or flounders were called calvers when treated thus.[70] Pickled salmon apparently kept all the year if the pickle was renewed every quarter.[71] Mackerel baked in vinegar would also keep a year if the juices were poured off and fresh vinegar poured on.[72] Jack and trout were especially 'agreeable varieties' for this treatment. Oysters were stewed in their own juice with vinegar and spices added. Then they were put in jars, the cold liquor poured on, and the tops covered with leather tied down. These kept good two or three months 'if the liquor is now and then boiled up, and poured on cold'. Cockles, mussels and winkles could be preserved likewise.[73]

A more palatable way to preserve salmon than by hard salting was by pickling it in vinegar sometimes with herbs and spices; preserved thus it was sold in London from Tudor times.[74] Fresh anchovies, imported from the Continent, had their heads taken off and were kept in vinegar, topped up as it evaporated; 'and this will preserve them from rotting for a year or two'.[75] The fish to be pickled could first be fried rather than boiled.[76] Hannah Glasse's 'To pickle Mackarel, call'd Caveach' is done this way, and the fried and pickled fish then covered with oil: 'They will keep well covered a great while, and are delicious'.[77]

**Pickling: Vegetables and Fruits**

Pickling in an acid solution, though known since ancient times, suddenly became extremely popular in sixteenth century England, and the same method was applied to every new fruit and vegetable arriving from new-found lands, and also to practically every other foodstuff. Verjuice and vinegar (the latter made from sour wine) both tasted like very sharp cider; alegar (made from sour ale or malt) was milder than modern malt vinegar, and pickles made with these acids were milder than modern ones.[78] However, until the nineteenth century, wine vinegar was preferred by the better-off for pickling as it had the best flavour. Vinegar could be made stronger for shipboard,[79] but for use in this country such vinegar was to be diluted to normal strength with an equal quantity of spring water. Strong distilled vinegar would preserve even raw vegetable stuffs such as walnuts and mushrooms:

> Mushrooms only wash them clean, dry them, and put them into little Bottles, with a Nutmeg just scalded in Vinegar, and sliced (whilst it is hot) very thin, with a few Blades of Mace; then fill up the Bottle with cold Vinegar and Spring-water, pour Mutton-fat try'd [rendered] over it, and tye a Bladder and Leather over the Top. These mushrooms won't be so white, but as finely tasted, as if they were just gathered; and a spoonful of this Pickle will give a Sauce a very fine Flavour.[80]

Spices, garlic, lemon peel and horseradish were often incorporated.

Hard water gave pickles a bad colour. Fruit and vegetables such as plums, kidney beans, samphire, cucumbers could be kept green by steeping in salt and vinegar, with alum sometimes added, in a brass or copper pan (but this caused verdigris poisoning).[81] It was discovered by some that the method of greening vegetables by repeatedly pouring on boiling vinegar had the incidental effect of preserving them much better than the usual method. Normally, the undistilled vinegar used for most pickles was poured cold onto the blanched or cooked vegetables or fruit, which had been allowed to go cold. This often meant that the pickle mothered and had to be boiled up periodically, and poured on again when cold.[82] John Evelyn recorded that his wife preferred a pickled cucumber recipe where the alegar and wine pickle was poured boiling hot over very close-packed 'gurkins' in a barrel once a day for three days: 'this keepes them long without changing and eate very excellently'.[83] Bailey (1736) also mentions a method which would ensure successful long keeping; in his recipe to preserve cucumbers he wrote 'every time any are taken out, make the rest scalding hot, and thus they may be kept for two or three years'.[84] It seems strange that in spite of the success of the hot method and the frequent poor results from the cold one, the importance of putting foods boiling hot into jars was not recognised.

Among other pickled vegetables were artichokes, asparagus, nasturtium seeds, ash keys, elder buds, mushrooms, onions, radish pods, cauliflowers, beetroots, artichoke suckers [young shoots] and samphire. Capers were imported and very expensive, but cheap home-grown substitutes were pickled broom buds and nasturtium seeds. Among fruits, quinces were pickled in vinegar, stale beer or wine, as were peaches, plums, nectarines and apricots, lemons, barberries, codlins and pippins, redcurrants damsons and grapes. Walnuts, gathered in late June before the shells formed, and pickled, were rich in vitamin C.

In view of the huge amounts of meat eaten and the small number of vegetables, pickles were an important garnish for the meat, visually, gastronomically and nutritionally. For example red cabbage in red wine vinegar 'will serve both for garnishing and for salad',[85] and pickled lemons or walnuts supplied a few vital vitamins. From the later seventeenth century, piccalilli and pickled mangoes were imported from India. Cheaper English imitation 'mangoes' were made with melons, pippins, onions, peaches, and cucumbers. The liquors from pickles such as walnut, lemon, mushroom, oyster and anchovy could be added to gravies and sauces, or used alone as a relish when they were given the name 'catsup'. Relishes and ketchups began to be sold commercially from 1760.[86] Innkeepers relied on a selection of ready-made pickles, relishes and ketchups to liven up their table of cold meats, potted meats, fish, and pies, and were among the first users of commercial sauces.

**Portable soup and travelling sauces** In the seventeenth century, recipes began to appear for a kind of dried instant soup, called pocket soup, cake soup, portable soup or veal glue. Ann Blencowe wrote down a recipe for it in her *Receipt Book* of 1694.[87] It was 'of extraordinary service to such as travel in wild and open Countries, where few or no Provisions are to be met with; and it will be of no less Benefit to such Families as have not immediate recourse to Markets.'[88] It was made by boiling meat with skin and bones down to a glue-like consistency. The mass was dried and cut into convenient lumps, which when wanted, were simply reconstituted with boiling water. James Lind and Captain Cook introduced it into naval rations, but the naval version was no doubt crude, and men had to be flogged for refusing it.[89] Bradley wrote (1736): 'Some of this Cake-Gravey has lately been sold, . . . at some of the Taverns near *Temple-Bar*'.[90] The traveller could use it on feast days (i.e. meat days), while on fast days he might use bottled mushroom ketchup or travelling sauce. A travelling sauce was made with claret, vinegar, verjuice, salt, pepper, nutmeg, cloves, ginger, orange peel, mustard-seed, shallots, bayleaves, basil, marjoram, thyme and cinnamon infused with water over heat for twenty-four hours, then strained and put into stone bottles. It would keep for twelve months. 'This is a good Companion for travellers who more frequently find good Meat than good Cooks.' Another useful and convenient seasoning for travellers was dry vinegar to carry in the pocket. A recipe of 1615 runs: 'Take the bladder [inflated pericarp] of green corn, either wheat or rye, and beat it in a mortar with the strongest vinegar you can get, till it is as paste. Roll it into balls, drie them in the sun, and when you need vinegar, cut a piece and dissolve it in wine, or water to make vinegar'.[91] Other convenient condiments for travellers were mustard balls – mustard seed ground into flour, mixed with honey and canary, made into little balls and dried. Hartlib wrote 'at Tewxbury the best kind of mustard made up into cakes and rowles, a little [vinegar] being put to what is scraped off, you have an excellent mustard.'[92]

Putrefactive bacteria require water and a suitable temperature in order to grow, and so drying was an effective way of preserving foods. In dark-age Europe, strips of meat were dried between horse and saddle on long journeys and then eaten raw. Vidame de Chartres, in the time of Edward VI, observed that the Scots ate raw deer's flesh which had been pressed between two flat pieces of wood until hard and dry.[93] On St Kilda a traveller in 1698 observed the air-drying of Solan geese and gannets.[94] Mushrooms were dried on strings by the fire, then crushed to powder and kept in dry bottles with wide necks, close-stopped, to use in sauces.[95] Artichoke bottoms were dried in the oven till as hard as wood. When needed they were steeped in water for twenty-four to forty-eight hours and boiled until done when 'they will eat as well as if fresh cut'.[96] Yeast was dried on the twigs of a birch whisk; when wanted for brewing the whisk was thrown into the wort. Yeast was also dried by being painted in successive layers onto a plate or inside a tub, to a depth of two or three inches, care being taken to keep off dust. It could still be reactivated after several months.[97]

It was also effective to bury foods, both to exclude air and to keep them cool. Eggs were kept in sand, bran, ashes, sawdust or meal; walnuts and citrus fruit were kept in sand; hazelnuts were kept in dry earth, and grapes kept in oats.[98]

A further way of preserving vegetables was with salt; in the eighteenth century, green beans were layered with salt, and cabbage was made into sauerkraut in imitation of that made by North Europeans.[99] This too was introduced into navy rations by Captain Cook and resisted by the sailors. In the mid-seventeenth century it was noted that Spanish and

**Drying and other methods of preservation**

85

Italian sailors enjoyed a much better shipboard diet than their English counterparts partly because of their imaginative use of olive oil. Gradually recipes began to appear for such vegetables as artichokes and mushrooms preserved in olive oil, called 'The Spanish Way' or 'The Italian Way'.[100]

Cold and ice act as preservative agents by slowing down the growth of bacteria. Ice-houses were in use in Italy in the sixteenth century, and were built in England in the late seventeenth century, but ice was used mainly for cooling drinks and making iced desserts.[101] The Chinese were observed by members of the East India Company to pack their fish in snow to send inland, and in 1786 the Scots began to pack salmon in boxes of ice for shipment to London. In 1666, Robert Boyle tried experiments 'to produce cold without snow, ice, hail, wind or nitre'[102] (saltpetre water had been used for cooling drinks). At another time he made trials of freezing ox gall, sheep's blood, milk, eggs, eels in vinegar, oranges, lemons, and onions, besides other items.[103] Ice was first produced mechanically in 1775 when Dr Cullen produced small amounts by means of a very high vacuum; but this was insufficient for preserving purposes.

*Potting*   One of the new techniques of the sixteenth century, potting, worked on the principle of smothering the food to be preserved totally in melted fat, usually butter, lard or mutton fat, in order to exclude the air, in a pot or cask, which was then sealed tightly. This apparently worked sufficiently frequently to merit wide application even for use on shipboard in hot climates, as described by Boyle in 1663.[104] Sir Hugh Platt described the process as practiced about 1600 or earlier:

> Some do use to parboil their Fowl, after they have taken out the garbage, and then do dip them in Barrowsgreace [lard], or in clarified butter, till they have gotten a new garment over them, and then they

lay them one by one in stone pots, filling the stone
pots up to the brim with Barrows greace or clarified
Butter.

The fowl were flavoured with cloves and salt, stopped very
close and kept in a cool place 'and they will keep sweet and
good a moneth together'.[105]
Potting was merely a development of pie-making. Huge
pie crusts of hard rye paste had been used for baking very
large joints. When cooked, the gravy was poured off, the
spaces filled with clarified butter, with a thick layer of
butter on top, and the lid replaced. These pies could be
sent great distances without harm, or would keep in a cold
place for up to a year. Rabisha's recipe 'to Bake Venison in
Crust, or in Pots' and 'to Collar Venison' illustrate the
transition from paste to earthenware.[106] 'This is as rich
and honourable a second-course dish, as your Brawn is for
the first.' Venison pies were difficult to keep about
midsummer; Sir Kenelm Digby thought it was because of
the 'sympathy' between the potted meat and its friends and
relatives capering about and mating in its native park.[107]
Recipes abound in the seventeenth and eighteenth centuries
for potting beef in imitation of venison, which indicate the
consistently high regard for the latter.
Seafood, fish and birds of all kinds were potted.[108] Even
raw poultry and raw pork could be potted – a correspondent
to Richard Bradley wrote from Suffolk saying she had kept
raw pigeons this way for a month, and Ellis reported 'A
Yorkshire Cook-Maid's Way to Pickle Pork', which was to
rub the raw pieces with sugar, salt and saltpetre and then
to pot the meat under fat: 'No way exceeds this'.[109] Potting
was a useful method for preserving garnishes such as
cockscombs which may have been difficult to obtain in
quantity at a moment's notice. Other foods were potted for
shipboard, such as giblets, lettuces, and peas bottled in
mutton fat.[110]
In the early eighteenth century it was found that meats,

fish and cheese to be potted would keep even longer if mashed up with butter first.[111] Bradley said that potted meats were especially useful in April: 'This is . . . a time of the Year when potted Meats begin to come into fashion,' i.e. before animals were in best condition to be slaughtered.[112] Inns found potted foods especially useful for a constant cold board, cut in thin slices to be served with vinegar or a variety of pickles.[113] Even gravy could be potted: Ann Cook discovered a successful way of potting gravy so that it could be brought out when serving salt beef. Juices from a baked piece of fresh meat were boiled to a stiff jelly, then poured into one-pint jars or pots and each covered with boiled-up beef fat. Gravy prepared in this way would keep two months, but would last six months if boiled to glue.[114]

In potting, the quality of the butter was of paramount importance. Hannah Glasse continually exhorted in her potting recipes: 'Let your Butter be very good, or you will spoil all'.[115] A great deal of butter must have been rancid, for even heavily-salted butter would spoil if not kept very cold. It seems strange that clarified butter was little known. Clarified butter keeps well even in hot climates. Court cooks, such as Rabisha, influenced by Continental cooking used it, but outside Court circles it was not well known, and it was not on sale. A correspondent wrote to Hartlib that if butter were clarified, 'many hundreds of firkins may be saved. And besides it is saving very much in housekeeping where they used to spend foolishly so much of fresh butter'.[116] Like butter, cheese could also be preserved in salt or brine, and was preserved in this way for the navy after 1758. However, both butter and cheese barrelled for the navy often went bad even before being put on board ship.

***Early Methods for Preserving Fruit*** In the sixteenth century, sugar had become more easily available and was used increasingly in the preparation of luxury banqueting stuffs, including preserved fruits, roots, stems and flowers. The advantage of these foods was that they could be kept for months, or even years, in a dry still-room and brought out as occasion demanded. Wet sweetmeats were preserved in syrup in jars, and dry sweetmeats, dried fruits, dried candied fruits, stems, roots, peels and stiff marmalades were kept in boxes. Fruits for the banquet were generally preserved whole or in large pieces to retain a pretty appearance, and were called 'preserves'. 'Conserves', jams and marmalades were usually mashed.[117] Jam seems to be a peculiarly English pheno-menon, a product perhaps of English culinary amateurish-ness, or one result of the cheaper sugar flooding in after 1650 from English colonies.

From the sixteenth century, firm, slightly unripe fruits such as pear-plums, damsons, apricots, peaches and cherries were put directly into boiling syrup or boiling fruit jelly, which kept them in shape.[118] Fruits boiled two or three times over in very heavy syrups and jellies became candied and could be taken out, dried off in a cool oven and boxed, but these tasted more of sugar than of fruit. Using an alternative method, the sugar was boiled 'to a candy height' (240°F, 115°C) and beaten, at which point it turned into hard candy. The raw fruit was dropped on to this, and heated very gently whereupon it 'melted' the hard candy, and became lightly cooked while remaining juicy and much superior in flavour to modern 'preserves'. The temperature of the fruit is raised only enough to release the pectin and produce a set without the fruit ever being brought to the boil: hence the excellent flavour and colour.[119] (The method is still used in Upper Provence.)[120] The result, as Hilary Spurling found when editing *Elinor Fettiplace's Receipt Book* of 1604, is superior jam made with whole fruit.[121] The recipes use equal quantities of sugar and fruit, and test for setting by trying a few drops on a trencher in exactly the same way as those for modern jam.

It was difficult to preserve fruit without sugar, but there was a real need, for, as Boyle said, too much sugar 'clogs most men's stomachs'. All kinds of methods had been tried: by burying the raw fruit in sand, sawdust, hay or oatmeal, by drying, by hanging on strings, by laying fruit in cold running streams, by keeping it in wine, beer or vinegar solutions, or by dipping it in wax; but these only delayed the rot and could not prevent it. The keeping of raw fruits in tightly closed pots in cold, dry cellars may have sometimes been successful if the fruit was very clean and sound, for in airtight conditions it would continue to respire and so create carbon dioxide. A concentration of twenty per cent would have been successful. (Carbon dioxide storage of fruit is used today, but is very expensive.) A typical recipe is this of 1682:

> To keep Goosberries green and fresh, so that you
> may make a green Goosberry-tart at Christmas.
> Take green Goosberries when they are full grown,
> put them fresh gathered without much handling
> them, into Stone-Bottles; stop them very close, and
> put store of wax about the Corks, then bury the
> Bottles in the ground, or under a heap of Coals in
> the Cellar, and they will keep fresh and green all
> Winter long.[122]

The simplest way to preserve fruit without sugar was to dry it, but the English climate prevented sun-drying. Apples such as Norfolk biffins, pears or plums could be dried whole in cooling bread ovens over several successive days, care being taken that they did not burst and lose their juice. Apples could be sliced and dried on strings[123] but not much fruit-drying was done. John Beale wrote to Hartlib February 16th 1656–7 complaining of English wastefulness and added 'Noe plums ever dryed, nor peares, except in fewe houses'.[124] Fruit drying was one of the activities the Agricultural Committee of the Royal Society sought to encourage (1664), but generally fruit-growing areas were not cheap fuel areas. Hartlib reported that dried pippins, pears and prunellas were imported from France. The French were able to preserve fruit without sugar also in wine, wine-must or cider, boiled down until a few drops set on a plate, and they boiled grape juice and grape flesh without sugar to make jelly. Alcohol was used as a preservative for fruit, for example, brandied peaches.[125] The germicidal action is most effective at fifty per cent concentration, but since the fruit juices would dilute it a much stronger proof such as ninety per cent was needed.

The use of preserved fruits was rare except among the wealthier classes. Commercially preserved fruit was expensive. Thomas Turner, the Lewes Sussex shopkeeper, ate preserved fruits, usually in tarts, only half a dozen times in winter, always at festive parties in company with his friends of the 'middling' sort, all comfortably well-off.[126] Most people simply did not eat fruit in winter at all, except apples and a little dried fruit in puddings. Poorer people would only have a few raisins and currants at Christmas.

Among the hundreds of preserving recipes there is one that leaps off the page for the modern reader. It is the bottling of gooseberries and such small fruits without sugar by a method which ensured that the fruits would be sterile, but of course this was not understood, and the recipe, though declared successful, was not given more prominence than others. This is Hannah Glasse's recipe (1747):

**The Origins of Fruit-bottling**

> *To keep Green Gooseberries till Christmas*
> Pick your large green Gooseberries on a dry Day,
> have ready your Bottles clean and dry, fill the
> Bottles and cork them, set them in a kettle of Water
> up to their Neck, let the Water boil very softly till
> you find the Gooseberries are coddled, take them
> out, and put in the rest of the Bottles till all is done;
> then have ready some Rosin melted in a Pipkin, dip

the Necks of the Bottles in, and that will keep all
Air from coming in at the Cork, keep them in a cool,
dry Place, where no Damp is, and they will bake as
red as a Cherry.[127]

The novel way of boiling corked bottles of fruit up to their
necks is very striking, and is of course still in use today.
Fruit bottles now have wide necks, but some poorer
communities in Europe were, until recently, still using
wine bottles to preserve fruit. Hannah Glasse copied her
recipe word for word from Eliza Smith's *The Compleat
Housewife* (1727); Eliza Smith and Bradley (1727) may
have found theirs in a book of 1705, William Salmon's
*The Family Dictionary* in which he specifies the use of
'jars'. The 'bottles' mentioned by Smith and Glasse imply
they were bottles with narrow necks, especially as the
fruits specified are only those small enough to be pushed
into such a bottle. Bradley advised the ordering of 'Quart
Bottles that are made on purpose with large wide Necks' (a
quart was 32 oz).[128] An even earlier version of the recipe
appeared in *The Book of Receipts According to Our
Newest Methods* (1680). Earlier still (1663) Robert Boyle
wrote:

I may . . . tell you of an eminent Naturalist, a Friend
of yours and mine, that hath a strange way of
preserving Fruits, whereby even Goos-berries have
been kept for many Moneths, without the addition
of Sugar, Salt, or other tangible Bodies; but all that I
dare tell you, is, That he assures me his Secret
consists in a new and artificiall way of keeping them
from the Air.[129]

Was this really the source of the first sterile bottling
method, developed by a scientist in a laboratory? From
1645, Boyle was in touch with the 'invisible college',
which became the Royal Society in 1660. Since the 1630s,

Samuel Hartlib had been the focus of a large part of this group actively trying, among many other experimental activities, to improve food production and preservation. Boyle himself had preserved 'an entire Puppy, of pretty bigness, untainted for many weeks' in alcohol, and conserved various foods '*in vacuo*' by means of his air pump. In May 1669 he wrote that 'a peice of Rosted Beife seald up Sept ye 15 1668 appeard to be not at all alter'd As did likewise a peice of Cheese seald up in another [vessel] and some peices of a french Role ye same day Sept 15 seald up in a third.'[130] A recipe book of the 1690s shows an attempt to preserve soft berries in stoneware bottles heated 'to draw out as much of the air as may be', but without success.[131] Considering the date of the earliest printed recipe for the sterile bottling of gooseberries I have so far found, 1680, it is quite surprising to see that, in 1808, Thomas Saddington was awarded five guineas for the same recipe by the Society of Arts 'for a cheap method of preserving fruit without Sugar, for house use and sea stores'.[132] His only 'improvement' was to specify a temperature of 160°F or 170°F. Saddington had a small-scale enterprise going, which, however, was soon overtaken by the more professional methods of the Frenchman Nicolas Appert.

Appert experimented with champagne bottles in a water bath, and then with wider-necked bottles, using fruit, meat and vegetables. In Holland, tinned iron containers were tried; in the 1770s roast beef, covered with dripping and put in a tin box, was sent to Dutch Guinea, a fact discovered by Dr D. Dickinson in Stedman's *Diaries* 1772–77, and 'it may be suggested that in order to eliminate all the contaminating air, the canister was placed on a hot hob to boil and drive off any air nestling in the folds of the joint. This would have the effect of leaving a top layer of fat immediately below the tin lid'.[133] This *may* have been a development from an unusual method of cooking mentioned by Hannah Glasse whereby spinach or peas could be cooked in a water-tight tin box in a boiling cauldron. Such a box of cooked food, if inadvertently put aside, would be found to be perfectly preserved.[134]

Food was cooked within other kinds of closed vessels placed in cauldrons of boiling water; flagons of meat closed with paste were boiled to extract the juices for invalid fare (the delicate method was thought to preserve the 'spirituous parts' or vital properties of the food). If these flagons were set aside the contents would keep sound for some time.[135] In *A Closet for Ladies and Gentlemen* (1611), a cock is stewed in a stopped-up 'glassen pot'. It had also become the occasional practice to cook fruit in a tall, closed pot set in a bath of boiling water, before re-boiling the fruit with sugar.[137] Another way to cook fruits in their own juice was in a jar in the oven, and among Evelyn's manuscript papers is this recipe:

> To keep Damsons all the yeare
> Bake two potts of Damsons when they are baked fill
> one pot with as many of the other as is convenient
> leave as much space as you may put some melted
> butter on the top to cover them be sure they have
> sirup enough of their owne to cover them then the
> butter, cover the pot with a paper tyed downe.[138]

Evelyn, a member of the Royal Society and friend of Boyle, experimented widely in growing fruit and vegetables both old and new. It was no wonder that 'his wife is admirable in the way of preserving conserving etc and for all manner of sweetmeats most rare'.[139] The Evelyns' damson recipe would be entirely successful; the method was still widely in use until the mid-twentieth century, mutton fat being the usual sealant in England (in America paraffin wax was used).

A French recipe of 1616 is unusual when it says 'you must put up your Cherries into their glasse good and hot for to be kept'.[140] Most food was put into preserving jars cold, and mould was expected and dealt with by periodically boiling up the syrup or liquor, which must have proved onerous. Taking the covers off to inspect regularly would have undone even a successful preserve. Many recipes are hair-raising, such as Bradley's for bottled pigeons: 'When your Pidgeons are boil'd tender enough, take them from the Fire, and when the Liquor is cold, lay your Pidgeons in a large Gally-pot, and pour the Liquor upon them, and cover them up close with Leather, and they will keep a long time'.[141] Food poisoning must have been frequent. Not all food poisoning induces diarrhoea and vomiting; some forms produce swollen glands, headaches or paralysis – symptoms which would not necessarily be associated with a recent meal, and so the food would not come under suspicion. Many recipes mentioned the possibility that food may rot, putrefy, hoar, cloud, rope, sour, corrupt, or go rank, rusty, foisty, musty, mouldy, mothered, tainted, fly-blown, or maggoty, and suggested ways of overcoming these faults by scalding or boiling up, or wiping and repotting, or eating immediately. Ellis recommended that slightly tainted meat should be cooked with a quantity of root vegetables and onions so that the taste would not be noticed. Hannah Glasse has recipes entitled 'How to save potted birds that begin to be bad' and 'To Keep Venison or Hares sweet; or to make them fresh, when they stink'.[142] Markham's remedy was to lay the tainted venison for twelve hours in a pickle of strong ale, wine vinegar and salt, then to parboil it in water, season with salt and pepper, and bake it.[143] Another well-known remedy for tainted venison was described by Sir Hugh Platt, who recommended cutting off the green bits, boning it, and burying it in the earth for twelve to twenty hours.[144]

Air (later oxygen) was thought to be the cause of putrefaction. However, there seemed to be no difficulty in

**When preserving methods failed**

accepting that some foods could be preserved by actually hanging them in the air. Although in the seventeenth century microbes had been seen and described by Leeuwenhoeck and others using microscopes, their nature was not understood. The periodic boiling up of syrups and liquors was done without any understanding of how this postponed decay. It was not until 1776 that Spallanzani showed by experiment that putrescible materials could be fully preserved by boiling them in a sealed flask (after at least one hundred years of successful empirical culinary practice), and not until 1857 that Pasteur proved that microbes were responsible for putrefaction. Great pains were taken to exclude the air, jars were filled to the rim where possible, and the foods kept submerged below the liquor, oil or fat. Paper circles cut just to fit were laid on the tops of preserves, and jars were covered with paper or leather. Pickle jars were covered with first a bladder then a leather; but though bladder, especially when wet, was a tighter fit than leather, neither could prevent evaporation and so a lath was often placed on top, and the pickles periodically filled up with vinegar.[145]

Until 1800, most of the improvements in food preservation benefitted those who were comfortably-off. The food of the army and navy remained a source of huge dissatisfaction, being largely unchanged from Tudor times, until the early nineteenth century when tinned meat was introduced. By 1790 the food of working people in the south of England had actually deteriorated, their pottage and ale of Tudor times having been replaced by white bread and cheese and tea, while the Welsh and northerners continued to subsist on oatmeal, herbs, vegetables, bacon and the occasional piece of fresh meat as they had done for centuries. Most working people did not have the wherewithal to make, or buy preserved fruits or jams; even currants at 8d a lb in the 1760s were beyond their reach.[146] The trade depression from the 1790s to the 1840s ensured that no such luxuries would be forthcoming during that

## Necessities and Luxuries

time except on special occasions. The well-off alone continued to enjoy their hams, tongues, potted meats and fish, pickles, sauces, jams, and preserved fruits and vegetables until the mid-nineteenth century. It was then that massive imports of sugar from the West Indies necessitated a huge industry to use it up, and this was found in the making of cheap jam, which from 1870 was to replace vitamin-rich butter on the subsistence bread of factory workers.[147]

1. Mary McLeod Innes, 'Scottish student fare in the sixteenth century as revealed by the St Andrews Diet Books', *Petits Propos Culinaires* 28 (1988), p. 41.
2. Elizabeth David, *Spices, Salt and Aromatics in the English Kitchen* (Penguin 1970), p. 165. We tend to excuse our lack of cuisine by saying the excellent quality of our fresh meat did not require ingenuity in the dressing of it.
3. Sir John Fortescue, *The Difference between an Absolute and Limited Monarchy* (London, 1714), p. 73. French and Continental books on cookery and rural economy translated into English give a false picture of foods being preserved in England as they were really describing Continental practices. Among these were *Palladius of Husbondrie* (Early English Text Society, ES 52, 1873), a fourth-century text translated into English soon after 1400; Noel Chomel, *Dictionaire Oeconomique or, The Family Dictionary*, revised by Richard Bradley, 2 vols. (London, 1725); Charles Estienne and Jean Liébault, *Maison Rustique or, The Countrey Farme* translated by Richard Surflet, revised by Gervase Markham (London, 1616); F. P. de la Varenne, *The French Cook (Cuisinier françois)* 3rd edn. (London, 1673); F. Massialot, *The Court and Country Cook (Cuisinier roial et bourgeois)* (London, 1702); F. Massialot, *New instructions for Confectioners (Nouvelle instruction pour les confitures)* (London, 1702); V. La Chapelle, *The Modern Cook's and Complete Housewife's Companion* (London, 1736).
4. Dr Martin Lister, *A Journey to Paris in the Year 1698* (London, 1698): extract printed in *Petits Propos Culinaires* 22 (1986), p. 33; William Ellis, *Country Housewife's Family Companion* (London, 1750), p. 108; C. Anne Wilson, *Food and Drink in Britain* (Penguin, 1976) pp. 38; 48; Reay Tannahill, *Food in History* (New York, 1973), pp. 212–14; Charles Lucas, *An Essay on Waters* (London, 1756), II, p. 36. Scottish salt was bitter from magnesium salts and caused 'saltburn' on fish.
5. Hannah Glasse, *The Art of Cookery Made Plain and Easy* (London, 1747), p. 130; Glasse, 6th ed., 1758 Appendix Zz.

97

6. Robert Boyle, *Some Considerations touching the Usefulness of Experimental Naturall Philosophy* (London, 1663), pt. II, p. 109.

7. Glasse (1747, reprinted London, 1983), pp. 194; 197.

8. Glasse (1747), pp. 128–9; John Nott, *The Cook's and Confectioner's Dictionary* (London, 1723), BE 53; Nathan Bailey, *Dictionarium Domesticum (Household Dictionary)* (London, 1736).

9. Ellis, p. 108.

10. Andrew Boorde, *A Compendyous Regyment, or A Dyetary of Helth, 1542*, ed. F. J. Furnivall (Early English Text Society, ES 10, 1870), pp. 269; 292; 271; *Thomas Tusser, His Good Points of Husbandry*, ed. D. Hartley (London, 1931), p. 71. Tusser's first edition was 1557.

11. Wilson (1976) pp. 46; 49; G. Hartman, *The True Preserver and Restorer of Health, part 2: Excellent Directions for Cookery* (London, 1684), p. 59.

12. Randle Holme, *The Academy of Armory* (London, 1688), Book III, p. 81.

13. Rev. J. G. Wood, *The Illustrated Natural History*, 1863, in T. Stobart, *The Cook's Encyclopaedia* (London, 1980), p. 363.

14. T. Muffett, *Healths Improvement* (London, 1655), pp. 154–5.

15. Hartman, p. 59.

16. Dorothy Hartley, *Food in England* (London, 1954, 1973), p. 253.

17. Tusser (1931) pp. 139; 118.

18. Thomas McLachlan, 'History of Food Processing', *Progress in Food and Nutrition Science* (Oxford, 1975), vol. I, pp. 461–91.

19. Wilson (1976), p. 38.

20. A.W., *A Booke of Cookry Very Necessary for All Such as Delight Therein* (London, 1584), p. 4.

21. Sir Hugh Platt, *The Jewel-house of Art and Nature*, new ed. (London, 1653), p. 71.

22. Wilson (1976), p. 47; Glasse (1747), p. 155; Nott, A 49.

23. Ellis, pp. 49; 86.

24. Bailey, BE

25. Ellis, pp. 222–3.

26. Richard Bradley, *The Country Housewife and Lady's Director*, pt. I, 6th edn. (1736, reprinted London, 1980), p. 187.

27. Ellis, pp. 69–70; Wilson (1976), p. 96: 'The Martinmas 'mart' and the occasional 'braxy' (a sheep which had died naturally, often of braxy, a form of colic, and thereafter been salted) were said to be the only butchers' meat eaten by the poor of Scotland at that period'. (E. Burt, *Letters from a Gentleman in the North of Scotland*, new edn., 2 vols., 1815, vol. 1, p. 113.)

28. Ruth Strong, 'Pudsey fare: food in the Pudsey district from the early seventeenth century to c. 1840', *Old West Riding* vol. 6, no. 1, p. 29; Frank Peel, *Spen Valley: Past and Present* (Heckmondwike, 1893), p. 212; Hartley, p. 322.

29. *Ann Cook and Friend*, ed. Regula Burnet (London, 1940), p. 17. (Ann Cook, *Professed Cookery* first appeared in 1754.)

30. See the papers of Samuel Hartlib, from the 1630s at the centre of a wide circle of natural philosophers, the 'invisible college', which formed the nucleus of the Royal Society at its foundation in 1660. The papers are at the University of Sheffield. I examined mainly the Ephemerides which contain summaries of facts and findings on a multitude of subjects sent by correspondents to Hartlib between 1634 and 1659. There are longer papers on Oeconomica Culinaria and Oeconomica Domestica. The Hartlib Project is in process of transcribing the papers onto disk.
31. Ellis, pp. 95–6.
32. Hartlib, Ephemerides.
33. In 1931 a patent was taken out by the Germans for the method. This patent was infringed by the Poles who, when tackled, proved its old origin and the patent was then void. Most bacon is now injected. (McLachlan, p. 477).
34. Ellis, p. 97; Nott B 7; Glasse (1747), p. 130.
35. Ellis, p. 97. There is a tradition that the first bacon factory in Britain began in 1770 when John Harris of Calne, Wiltshire, watched pigs resting there on their way from Ireland to London and had the idea of curing them on the spot (see Tom Stobart, *The Cook's Encyclopaedia*, London, 1980, p. 29). This is evidently inaccurate.
36. Ellis, pp. 98–100.
37. Tusser (1931), p. 161.
38. Holme, Book III, p. 81; *England's Happiness Improv'd* (London, 1699), p. 167.
39. John Evelyn MS Book IIII Receipts of Cookery, Christ Church College, Oxford; W. Rabisha, *The Whole Body of Cookery Dissected*, 2nd ed. (London, 1673), p. 82.
40. Ellis, p. 111. It is a popular myth that York hams were reputed to have gained their fine flavour from being smoked over the chips and sawdust produced during the building of York Minster.
41. Bradley, pt. I glossary, pp. 77–8.
42. Nott B 7; Ellis, pp. 110–15.
43. Ellis, pp. 110; 112.
44. Glasse (1747), p. 130.
45. Hartley, p. 322.
46. Glasse (1747) p. 130; Tusser (1931) p. 137.
47. Glasse (1747) p. 129.
48. Bradley, Part I, p. 164.
49. Wilson (1976), p. 117.
50. Bailey, PO.
51. Ellis, pp. 58–60; 113.
52. Ellis, p. 60; Evelyn, MS Book IIII p. 26. There was a curious superstition, which persisted until the mid-twentieth century in country districts, that menstruating women, or those recovering from childbirth, must not take part in salting meat. Bradley wrote: 'As for the Common Notion, that Women cannot lay

Meat in Salt, equally with success, at all Times, it is false; it is the Manner of doing it, and not the state of the Women who handle it, that makes it right.' Pt. II, pp. 2; 3; Hartley, p. 325.

53. Ellis, pp. 31; 48; 51; 52.
54. Ellis, pp. 69; 70.
55. Ellis, p. 119; Bradley, pt. I, pp. 182; 186; Sir Kenelm Digby, *The Closet Opened*, 3rd edn., 1677, ed. A. Macdonnell (London, 1910), pp. 205-6.
56. Bradley, pt. I, p. 182; Ellis, p. 120.
57. Robert May, *The Accomplisht Cook*, 4th ed. (London, 1678), p. 194; Digby (1910) pp. 205-6; Bradley, pt. I, p. 63; Ellis, p. 124.
58. Bradley, pt. I, p. 111; Ellis, p. 124.
59. Wilson (1976), p. 95; Elizabeth Raffald, *The Experienced English House-Keeper*, 2nd ed. (Manchester, 1771), p. 259.
60. Bradley, pt. I, p. 63.
61. Ellis, p. 61.
62. Glasse (1747), p. 128.
63. Bradley, pt. I, p. 63.
64. Holme, Book III, p. 82.
65. Wilson (1976), p. 123; Eliza Smith, *The Compleat Housewife* (London, 1727), p. 61.
66. Glasse (1747), p. 55; Wilson (1976), p. 95.
67. Glasse (1747), p. 128.
68. Glasse, 6th ed. (1758), p. 379.
69. Glasse (1747), pp. 116; 128; Bradley, pt. I, p. 37.
70. Holme, Book III, p. 82.
71. Nott S 31.
72. Glasse (1747), p. 116; Bradley, pt. I, p. 66.
73. Bradley, pt. I, pp. 166; 168-9; Hartley, p. 279.
74. Wilson (1976), p. 47.
75. Bailey, AN.
76. Holme, Book III, p. 83; Evelyn MS Book IIII, recipe 96.
77. Glasse (1747), p. 130.
78. Platt, p. 68. Modern malt vinegar has a higher acetic acid content than that manufactured even fifty years ago because of the new high starch barleys, improved conversion of these starches to sugar in malting, more efficient fermentation of the sugars and improved acetification, (McLachlan, p. 473).
79. Glasse (1747), p. 157; Platt, pp. 179-80. Platt said a glass still should be used but many people used an ordinary leaden still which created 'an ill touch'.
80. Glasse (1747) p. 157.
81. Ellis gave a recipe (p. 116) 'To roast a gammon of bacon' which illustrates how hazardous to health cooking methods and utensils could be; the gammon was to be soaked for a day in wine in 'a glazed or pewter dish'. The glaze could very well have been lead glaze, so if the soaking wine had then been used in

cooking, three poisons could have been eaten – nitrites, formaldehyde and lead. Bradley, pt. I, pp. 117–20; Nott. PL 179, PL 186, PL 190.

82. Bradley, pt. I, p. 122.
83. Evelyn MS 52A, Christ Church Oxford, p. 33.
84. Bailey, CU.
85. William Rabisha, *The whole body of Cookery dissected*, 2nd ed. (London, 1675), p. 5.
86. Wilson (1976), p. 266; David (1970), p. 11.
87. Ann Blencowe, *Receipt Book, A.D. 1694* (London, 1925).
88. Bradley, pt. I, p. 58.
89. Lind used a very gentle evaporation of the meat juices set in bowls in a *balneum mariae* to avoid a rapid direct boiling which he thought would destroy the vital spirit (having deduced it was the freshness of food which cured scurvy). He made the first successful preservation of citrus fruit juice using the same method which of course preserved the vitamin C.
90. Bradley, pt. I, pp. 56; 58f.
91. Hartley, p. 653.
92. Bradley, pt. II (1732, reprinted London, 1980), p. 36; Nott M 74, 75; Hartlib, Ephemerides.
93. Hartley, p. 132; A. Riddervold and A. Ropeid, eds., *Food Conservation*, Ethnological Studies (London, 1988), p. 215.
94. Wilson (1976), p. 104.
95. Bradley, pt. I, p. 146.
96. Glasse (1747) p. 156; Bradley, pt. I, p. 112.
97. Glasse (1747), p. 151.
98. Wilson (1976), pp. 126; 131; La Chapelle, p. 264; Hartley, p. 322.
99. Glasse (1747), p. 156; Ellis, p. 231; Glasse (1758), p. 376.
100. Hartlib, Dispensatoria Oeconomica; Boteler's *Dialogues*, 1634, ed. W. G. Perrin, Navy Records Society, 1930, p. 65; Glasse (1758) Appendix, p. 344; La Chapelle, p. 266.
101. Francis Bacon, *Sylva Sylvarum or A Naturall Historie* (London, 1626), para. 70; Evelyn MS Book IIII p. 11, recipe 59.
102. RBC 2.274, 11 July 1666, Royal Society Archives. Quotations from the Boyle Papers are reproduced by kind permission of the President and Council of the Royal Society.
103. Boyle, Commonplace Book 190, p. 15, Royal Society Archives.
104. Boyle (1663), pt. II, pp. 107–9.
105. Platt, p. 8.
106. Rabisha, pp. 23; 11.
107. William Hone, *The Table Book of Daily Recreation and Information* (London, 1827–28), p. 334.
108. e.g. Nott P 112; S 74; S 32.
109. Bradley, pt II, p. 87; Ellis, p. 63.
110. *William Salmon's Family Dictionary*, 4th ed. (London, 1710) p. 372; Nott P 58; Glasse (1747), p. 156; *The Whole Duty of a*

*Woman*, 1737, pp. 562–8; J. Middleton, *Five Hundred New Receipts in Cookery* (London, 1734). p. 119; Hartley, p. 390; La Chapelle, p. 265.

111.  Blencowe (1925), p. 21; May, p. 122; Charles Carter, *The Compleat City and Country Cook* (London, 1732), pp. 101–2; Glasse (1747), p. 252; Raffald, p. 253.
112.  Bradley, pt. I, p. 61.
113.  Bradley, pt. I, p. 64.
114.  Burnet, pp. 17–18.
115.  Glasse (1747), pp. 117; 128.
116.  Hartlib, Ephemerides.
117.  Many recipes for each style of preservation can be seen in contemporary recipe books, e.g. Estienne, revised Markham, *The Countrey Farme* (1616), II, li, pp. 349; 350; 425; *A Book of Fruits and Flowers, 1653* (reprinted London, 1984), pp. 36; 42; 43. They are discussed further in C. Anne Wilson, ed., *'Banquetting Stuffe'* (Edinburgh, 1991).
118.  Glasse (1747), p. 145.
119.  C. Anne Wilson, *in* Hilary Spurling, *Elinor Fettiplace's Receipt Book* (London, 1986), p. 129.
120.  Information from Christopher Driver.
121.  Spurling, p. 128.
122.  Hartman, p. 78.
123.  Bradley, pt. II, p. 118; Hartley, p. 414; Nott P 50, P 160.
124.  Hartlib 62/24/1A.
125.  Glasse (1747), p. 155.
126.  David Vaisey (ed.) *The Diary of Thomas Turner 1754–1765* (Oxford, 1984), pp. 137; 142; 171; 172; 194; 198; 199. The preserved fruits most used in these winter tarts were gooseberries, damsons, and bullaces. Turner and his friends also enjoyed at their parties raspberry puffs made with raspberry jam.
127.  Glasse (1747), p. 157; Ellis, p. 238.
128.  Bradley, pt. I, p. 104.
129.  Boyle (1663), pt. II, p. 106.
130.  Boyle, Short notes for Entrys (MS book 43) Royal Society Archives. My paper on Food Preservation and the Invisible College will appear in *Petits Propos Culinaires*.
131.  T. Tryon, *The Way to get Wealth*, 2nd ed. (London, 1702), 2, p. 79.
132.  *Transactions of the Royal Society of Arts* 26 (1808), pp. 145–52.
133.  McLachlan, p. 468.
134.  Glasse (1747), p. 99.
135.  Digby (1910), p. 141.
136.  *A Closet for Ladies and Gentlewomen* (London, 1611), p. 186.
137.  Hartman, p. 80.
138.  Evelyn MS Book IIII, p. 30, recipe 234.
139.  Hartlib, Ephemerides.
140.  Estienne, rev. Markham (1616), p. 422.
141.  Bradley, pt. II, pp. 88–9.
142.  Ellis, p. 51; Glasse (1747), pp. 8; 130.

143. G. Markham, *English Huswife*, 4th ed. (London, 1631), p. 113.
144. Platt, p. 20.
145. Glasse (1747), p. 133.
146. Strong, p. 31.
147. S. W. Mintz, *Sweetness and Power* (London, 1985), pp. 126–30; 148; 150; 186.

# 5.

## *Industrial food preservation in the nineteenth and twentieth centuries*

H. G. MULLER

**Introduction**  If kept beyond a certain period, most foods will deteriorate, often with changes in texture, taste and smell. More important still, poisonous products may be produced. There are several agents which can bring about these changes, but by far the most important are micro-organisms, so, essentially, food preservation is based on methods which kill micro-organisms, or at least stop them from multiplying, without making the food unsuitable for human consumption later.

There are basically five methods:

1. Chemical
2. Dehydration
3. Refrigeration
4. Canning
5. Atomic radiation.

All of these except atomic radiation were used or developed in the nineteenth century.

Food preservation has always been a matter of great public concern. It provides against want in periods of scarcity, particularly in cooler areas of the world which have only one annual harvest. It is also essential to equalise food distribution. Excess in one country may be used to supply the means of overcoming deficit in another.

**Chemical method**  In the nineteenth century, before the importance of micro-organisms was appreciated, a considerable number of chemicals were already known to prevent putrefaction. These were called antiseptics. Probably the first book on food preservation appeared in 1820 in Nuremberg. Written by J. C. Leuchs it listed thirty salts as well as twenty oils, spices and acids.[1] The most important chemical preservatives were sugar and salt.

The use of sugar or honey, which is much the same thing, is very ancient. In 1800 some archaeologists found in Egypt a large jar of honey. After thousands of years the honey still tasted perfect. Then some of the workers discovered some hairs in the honey, and when they tipped out the contents of the jar, they found a perfectly preserved baby. According to the *Alexander Romance*, the body of Alexander the Great was also preserved in honey during its long journey to Egypt.

Although sugar has been known since ancient times (Dioscorides calls it 'honey from reeds'), its use as a preservative only became significant in Europe after the eleventh century. Both in the nineteenth and in the present century it has been and is extensively employed in the preparation of marmalade and jam.

The other major chemical preservative was salt. The wealth of the Dutch and Hanseatic towns was built upon salt herrings, but that trade declined in the nineteenth century as better methods of food preservation were developed. Nevertheless, the picture (Figure 10) of salt packing of herrings in Lowestoft in *c.* 1900 shows that this method was still common. Among the old postcards which turn up in flea markets are many carrying similar views.

Meat also was widely salted and pickled. At the great exhibition in London in 1851, a whole pickled pig was exhibited (Figure 11). One still finds salted pork, beef and fish in a modern supermarket, but, with the exception of bacon, there is very little of it compared with the quantities of other preserved foods displayed there.

Alcohol has rarely been used as a preservative. It is true that the body of Lord Nelson was brought from Trafalgar

**10.**
Salt packing of
herrings in Lowestoft
*ca.* 1900.

in a barrel of brandy, and that one can find peaches in brandy on the delicatessen shelf. Nevertheless, brandy preserves are not part of a staple diet. There have always been better uses for alcohol.

Perhaps in this connection one should mention traditional fermentation. In different parts of the world a limited number of micro-organisms, mainly acid and alcohol

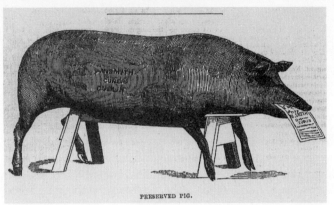

PRESERVED PIG.

**11.**
A whole pickled pig exhibited at the Great Exhibition in London in 1851.

producers, have been used to preserve food. This method is particularly effective in hot climates where other methods of preservation such as canning and refrigeration are not freely available.[2,3]

Today, chemical preservatives are far more effective than those used in past centuries. Except for sugar and salt, they are used in very small amounts. They include various acids, sulphur dioxide and its relatives, antibiotics and antioxidants. But during recent years chemical preservatives have been greatly reduced and, arguably as a result, cases of food poisoning in the UK have increased dramatically: 11,000 in 1976, and in 1987 30,000 with 50 deaths. It is assumed that only one case in ten is reported.

The relative risks due to food ingestion have been assessed as follows:[4]

| | |
|---|---:|
| Food-borne disease, i.e. food poisoning | 100,000 |
| Poor nutrition, i.e. deficiency disease | 100,000 |
| Environmental pollution | 100 |
| Natural toxicants (Cabbage family, pulses, spinach, bananas, almonds, cocoa etc.) | 100 |
| Pesticides | 1 |
| Additives | 1 |

In other words, the ratio of illness due to food poisoning to that due to food additives is 100,000 to one. The media would have us reverse these figures.

**Drying and dehydration**
By 'drying' one normally understands the withdrawal of moisture under natural conditions, e.g. sun- or wind-drying. Dehydration is the scientifically controlled removal of moisture by artificial means using steam, forced draught, conditioned air, etc.

Both drying and dehydration are accelerated by increasing the temperature of the food, but micro-organisms also grow better at slightly elevated temperatures. So when drying food, there is always a race between desiccation on the one hand, and bacterial growth on the other. If the temperature is low and bacteria do not grow well, relatively large pieces can be successfully dried. An example is the drying of stockfish in Canada and Scandinavia. If the temperature is high, the food to be dried must be small in size or thin. For instance, in the tropics thin strips of meat can be dried in the sun stretched out on barbed wire arrangements.

Figure 12i shows the sun drying of coffee beans *c*. 1880 and Figure 12ii in 1960. While the basic arrangement is the same, the increase in scale and efficiency is apparent.

The dried product is often greatly changed. Compare, for example, grapes with raisins, or plums with prunes. In medieval times and even in the sixteenth century when stockfish, like salt herrings, were a staple food, a stockfish hammer was a regular kitchen item: 'and when . . . it is desired to eat it [the stockfish], it behoves to beat it with a wooden hammer for a full hour . . .'.[5]

Artificial dehydration was already well established at the beginning of the nineteenth century. Leuchs[1] listed seven methods in 1820: drying on ovens or in baking ovens, in heated rooms, in a steam room, in a kiln, on a continuous wire band, in an oil or water bath and in a rotating wire cage (Drehrolle). He referred to drying in hot sand or ash

**12.**
i. Drying coffee
beans, *ca*. 1880.

**12.**
ii. Drying coffee
beans, *ca*. 1960.

but those methods were apparently obsolete in his day. Not so smoking. This is a very ancient preservation technique which is now mainly used to give a characteristic odour to the product (Figure 13). So far 130 compounds have been identified in wood smoke, and some of these have been shown to be carcinogenic. The greatest reduction of these

109

compounds has been achieved by using synthetic liquid smokes – aqueous solutions of the relevant chemicals, where objectionable components can be left out.[6]

An early British patent for artificial dehydration is that taken out by J. Graefer (1780) who blanched and then dried vegetables. There was also a 'Mr. Forsyth, the advocate, who cut potatoes and turnips into small pieces and heated them by steam on a metal plate'.

Edwards patented a process for drying vegetables in 1840 (BP 8597). The quality was poor, and when sent to the British troops in the Crimea in 1854–6 the dried vegetables did not prevent scurvy, presumably because vitamin C had been destroyed. Nevertheless, a considerable amount of dried vegetables was also used by the Union troops in the American civil war of 1861–5.

As regards meat, an important product originally invented by pre-Columbian Indians, and later used by both the British navy and North American explorers, was pemmican. Its preparation is described in the diary of Sir George Back in the 1830s: meat from deer or bison was cut into very thin slices, dried over the fire and pounded. Two parts of the meat were then mixed with one part of fat and the mixture stuffed into a bag made of animal hide. When combined with vegetables or oatmeal, two to three pounds would sustain a man for a day. Oatmeal, of course, contains an antioxidant, a chemical which tends to retard rancidity.

Apparently the first to evaporate meat broth were two French chemists, Joseph Proust and Antoine Parmentier. The product could be preserved either as a paste, or as slabs of a glue-like material. In 1938, Sir Jack Drummond analysed a cake of such 'portable soup' which had been made in 1771 (Figure 14). He concluded that it had been made from clear broth prepared from meat and bones. The journal *Chemistry and Industry* gives his analysis. The soup had shown no marked change in 160 years.

In 1848 the German chemist Justus von Liebig became

**13.**
Smoking strips of
moose in Canada,
*ca.*1880.

involved in the manufacture of meat extract. He published
his first experiments in that year, and realised the
commercial potential of utilising the vast South American
cattle herds to create a product for European use. In the
1840s there was no refrigerated transport and there was
no way of getting meat across the Atlantic. Animal skins
were sent as leather, but the carcasses were left to rot.
After Liebig's preliminary experiments the matter rested
until 1862. Then George Giebert, an engineer from Brazil,
met Liebig in Munich, and they discussed the practical
aspects of the large scale production of a meat extract.
F. X. Pettenkover then perfected the method of preparation,
and in 1864 Giebert established in Fray Bentos the first
small plant to produce meat extract on a commercial scale.
(Today most people associate the name of Fray Bentos
with corned beef: it is in fact a town in Uruguay.) Liebig
gladly gave his name to the venture, which became known
as Liebig's Extract of Meat Co. Ltd.

At first Giebert killed about 3000 head of cattle per

**14.**
Cake of portable soup made in 1771, and analysed in 1938 by Sir Jack Drummond. (By courtesy of the International Tin Research and Development Council.)

annum, a figure which by 1890 had risen to 56,000 head, to yield five million pounds of extract. In 1906 Liebig's Extract of Meat Co. Ltd. amalgamated with Brooke Bond and became Brooke Bond Liebig. In 1981 Liebig's name was dropped altogether and the company is now referred to as the Brooke Bond Group; from Liebig's meat extract was developed today's Oxo cube.

The enterprise did not have the lasting success that Liebig had hoped for. Firstly, the manufacture of the extract brought with it an unexpected decrease in nutrient value. The second reason was even more important: refrigerated transport of meat developed in competition. This was cheaper, gave a less denatured product, and reduced meat extract to the role of a condiment.

Modern methods of drying fall basically into four groups.[3] The first is tunnel-drying, which is a very common industrial method. Vegetables and fish are moved on a continuous band or in trollies through a heated tunnel. There are several sections in which airflow and temperature are carefully controlled.

The second is roller-drying. Here, semi-liquid foods, such as mashed potatoes, baby foods or milk, are dried between horizontal cylinders which are heated internally by steam under pressure. Two early patents are by Just-Hatmaker (BP 21,617) of 1902 and (BP 8743) of 1903.

The third method is spray-drying. A spray evaporator consists of a large chamber into which a fine spray of liquid is injected together with a current of hot air. The spray is almost instantly changed into a powder which is then separated from the moisture-laden air. An early patent is that of Ekenberg of 1909 (BP 16,375). The process is frequently used for the manufacture of coffee and milk powder.

The fourth process is referred to as freeze-drying, where the product (for instance, coffee) is frozen into blocks and the water removed under vacuum without melting. The process, which gives an excellent if expensive product, was first developed for biological materials in the 1950s.[7]

## Refrigeration

When one considers the history of refrigeration, what better way to start than with William Buckland (1784–1856), an Oxford professor of mineralogy and later Dean of Westminster, who served his unsuspecting guests meat from a frozen mammoth. 'Dear friends', he said, 'you have just eaten meat one hundred thousand years old . . .'. There had been great excitement in 1799 when a Tungus hunter found the first frozen mammoth in the ice in Siberia. The animal still had his last meal of grass and pine cones in his stomach (Figure 15). The famous French biologist Cuvier had identified the animal as ante-diluvian. Its skeleton is now in a museum in Leningrad and some shaggy hair was, and perhaps still is, in the Royal College of Surgeons in London.

Where the temperature is very low at some time of the

**15.**
Frozen mammoth
found in the ice in
Siberia in 1799.

year, as for instance in Russia or Canada, frozen meat has
long been an article of commerce. Here is a description of
the so-called frozen market in St Petersburg in 1800:

> There were partidges from Saratoff, swans from
> Finland, heath-cocks from Lavonia and Esthuria and
> geese from the steppes where Cossacks had killed
> them from horseback with their whips. All these
> birds were frozen, packed into chests and sold in the
> market. The freezing was so rapid that snow hares
> were frozen in an attitude of flight, with ears
> pointed and legs outstretched. Frozen reindeer or
> mighty elk with hairy snout stretched upon the
> ground and antlers raised majestically into the air,
> disappeared piece by piece as saw or axe separated
> them for distribution amongst the customers.[8]

Milk also frozen around a stick or loop of rope was sold in
the market.

Even in warmer climates food was often preserved in ice
houses. The Chinese already had them in 2000 BC. In

**16.**
Ice house near the old city wall in York.

Europe stately homes had ice-houses well before 1800, and in the United States there were public ice houses kept by the butchers. Figure 16 shows an ice-house near the old city wall in York. The deep shaft was filled with crushed ice or blocks of ice from the River Ouse. Interspersed were layers of straw or sawdust as insulation.

Some ice-houses were quite complicated. John Claudius Loudon, landscape gardener and writer on agricultural and architectural matters, designed one in the 1830s. It was fitted with five doors, a drain and cavity walls. If covered with a sufficient thickness of earth or straw, ice could be kept in this structure all year round.[9]

During the first quarter of the nineteenth century, natural ice became an article of commerce. There were two main sources, Wenham lake near Boston in the United States, and the Norwegian lakes. The very first commercial consignment was 180 tons and was sent from Boston to Calcutta in India. Of the 180 tons 80 were lost through melting, but the rest returned a good profit at 3d a pound.

To harvest the ice, the snow was first planed off and then a horsedrawn ice marker cut parallel grooves into the ice surface. (Figure 17). This was pulled first in one

**17.**
A horse-drawn ice-marker as used at Wenham Lake (see p. 115).

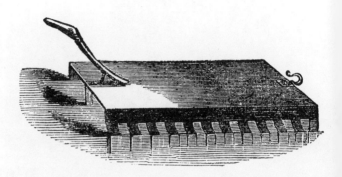

direction and then at right angles. Next an ice plow would deepen the grooves to 6'', and blocks would then be broken off with crowbars and wedges, and loaded directly on to seagoing vessels. Natural ice was used in the United States until well into the 1920s.

As regards the history of artificial refrigeration, two paths were followed: refrigeration by mechanical and by chemical means.[10] Only the former will be dealt with here because it is by far the most important.

If one wets one's hand and blows on it, the evaporation cools the hand. The harder one blows, the faster the evaporation, and the colder the hand.

Already in ancient times, people in India and Egypt placed flat, porous dishes filled with water on some dry grass to insulate them from the ground; and after a cool and windy night a layer of ice was formed. In fact the first British patent on refrigeration dated 15th January 1819 is based on this system.[11] However, the first systematic study of refrigeration was made by a Scot, William Cullen, professor of medicine and later of chemistry at Glasgow and Edinburgh. He published a paper in 1782 which begins as follows:

A young gentleman, one of my pupils, whom I had employed to examine the heat or cold that might be produced by the solution of certain substances in spirits of wine (alcohol), observed to me that when a thermometer had been immersed in spirits of wine, tho' the spirit was exactly of the temperature of the surrounding air, or somewhat colder, yet, upon taking the thermometer out of the spirit and suspending it in the air, the mercury in the thermometer, which was of Fahrenheits construction, always sunk two or three degrees . . . I suspected that water, and perhaps other fluids, in evaporating, produce or, as the phrase is, generate some degree of cold.[12]

Cullen made several experiments and when he placed a beaker of water inside a beaker of ether and the whole under vacuum, the ether evaporated so quickly, and the system got so cold, that to quote him: '. . . we found the most part of the water frozen and the vessel containing the ether surrounded by a thick and firm crust of ice . . .'.

The next step was taken by Jacob Perkins, an American and co-founder of the engineering firm of Baker-Perkins of Peterborough, since 1988 joint with APV and PASILAC. Amongst other things Perkins had been a steam specialist. On a miserable morning in December 1825 he demonstrated his steam-fired machine gun in Cumberland market before the Duke of Wellington.

> Five hundred balls a minute shot.
> Our foes in fight must kick the beam.
> Let Perkins only boil his pot
> And he'll destroy them all by steam.

The gun worked well enough, but the British army could not visualise stoking up a boiler during a surprise attack before the gun could be used. It was not a commercial success. His ice machine was not a commercial success

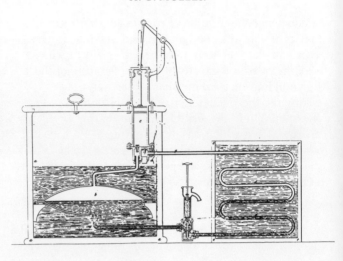

**18.**
Ice-machine designed
by Jacob Perkins in
1834: c (top centre):
compressor; d (right):
condenser; h (bottom
centre): expansion
valve; b (left):
evaporator.

either, although it did work (Figure 18). Patented in 1834
(BP 6662), it was based on the fact that on decompression
a gas will get cold and will therefore absorb heat. On
compression it will get hot – so Perkins built a jacketed
vessel containing water and with ether vapour in the jacket.
The pump in the centre, the compressor, would draw off
the vapour and compress it, so the vapour heated up. The
heat produced was now removed by a water cooled coil, the
condenser. The ether was then returned to the jacketed
vessel through the expansion valve whence it vapourised
and so cooled the water.

A modern refrigerator (Figure 19) has the same parts.
The evaporator is the deep-freeze cabinet and the
condenser, now air-cooled, is at the back of the cabinet.
The whole system is sealed, but the refrigerant is no longer
ether. In 1920, methyl chloride was first used as the
refrigerant, and in the 1930s, the freon types. It is expected
that these may soon be discarded because of their alleged
effect on the earth's ozone layer.

One of the first practical refrigeration plants was
developed by Henry and James (later Sir James) Bell and

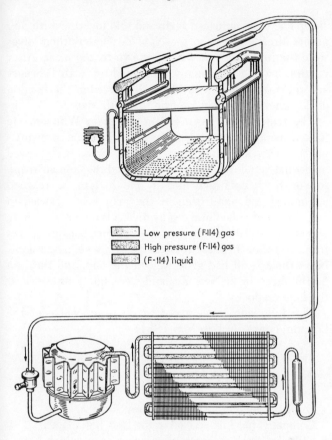

**19.**
Frigidaire domestic refrigerator, 1939 model: ice cabinet is the evaporator, bottom left the compressor, bottom right the condenser.

Low pressure (F-114) gas
High pressure (F-114) gas
(F-114) liquid

J. J. Coleman in consultation with Lord Kelvin, who at that time held the chair of natural philosophy at Glasgow. The Bell-Coleman patents were taken out in 1877, and the plant was first fitted to ships of the American and Australian runs.

Then New Zealand joined the trade. On 7th December 1881 the first sheeps' carcasses were loaded at Port Chalmers and frozen on board the SS Dunedin. On 11th December the engine's crank shaft broke and the first 641 sheep had to be unloaded again and sold together with 360 others already killed, so the New Zealanders themselves were the first consumers of their own frozen meat. After repairs, loading was finally completed on 11th February and the ship sailed on the 15th. It arrived at the London docks ninety-eight days later on the 24th May.

The trip had not been easy for Captain Whitson. He looked strained and careworn as he entered the company's office. The air circulation in the hold had proved inadequate, and the captain had entered the cold air trunk to cut fresh openings into it. He had to be rescued benumbed and half-frozen by the mate who crawled in after him and pulled him out by his heels on a rope. There was also concern that the masts would burn because sparks from the funnel had set fire to the sails on several occasions. Nevertheless, all had gone well in the end, and the first 5,000 sheep from New Zealand were safely unloaded at the London docks.

The following letter appeared on page twelve of the London Times on 27th May 1881:

FROZEN MEAT FROM NEW ZEALAND
To the Editor of the Times.
Sir, We beg to inform you that the sailing vessel
Dunedin, belonging to the Albion Shipping
Company, has just arrived in the East India Docks
with the first consignment of frozen meat which has
been sent to this country from New Zealand. This
shipment differs from all other importations of
frozen meat, from the fact of having been made in a
sailing vessel, which has been 98 days on the
passage, during which time the holds of the ship
containing the meat have been kept at about 20
degrees below freezing point. The vessel has on
board 5,000 sheep, and the apparatus for freezing
was fitted by the Bell-Coleman Mechanical
Refrigeration Company.

The meat is in fine condition, and the shipment has been managed by the New Zealand and Australian Line Company (Limited).

We consider this the most remarkable instance on record of what can be accomplished by mechanical refrigeration.

Yours faithfully,

WM. FRED. COTT,

for the Bell-Coleman Mechanical Refrigeration Company. 21 St Helen's-place, Bishopsgate within, May 25th.

In 1880, 400 cwt of frozen meat was imported into Britain from overseas. Only ten years later, in 1890 the amount had risen to 2.9 million cwt. To quote a contemporary: 'The frozen meat trade hangs on the slender piston rod of a refrigeration machine, yet feeds nations with a regularity that defies famine.'

Thus, by the end of the nineteenth century, the means of refrigeration were available. It had become clear that refrigeration was the only way to preserve food, so as to leave it more or less in its original state. Figure 20 shows the scale of modern food processing industries such as butter producers, which rely on refrigeration. There were, however, several unsolved problems. First, there was the difficulty of organising the refrigeration chain from producer to consumer. Transport was to remain the weak link for decades to come. Second, little was known about the effect of the rate of freezing and the conditions of the subsequent frozen storage. Work on these problems began during World War I. Finally, the actual means of heat transfer from the product had not been developed. Freezing took place in a cold room, and this is not very efficient. By the time of World War II three basic methods had been developed: the immersion bath or spray, the blast freezer and the plate freezer.

In the immersion bath the food, well wrapped, is

121

**20.**
A modern butter packaging plant. 25-kg blocks of butter stored at −10°C are raised by microwaves to +3° to 4°C in 16 seconds for reworking and packaging. (By courtesy of the Electricity Council.)

immersed in a refrigerated liquid, usually glycerol. With the spray method the product on a moving belt is sprayed with liquid nitrogen or a similar volatile refrigerant. In the blast freezer the product is subjected to a fast air stream at low temperature. In the plate freezer the product in square shape is squeezed between refrigerated plates. This freezer was developed by Clarence Birdseye.

Clarence Birdseye was born in Brooklyn, New York, in 1886. He went as a naturalist for the US government to Labrador between 1912 and 1916. He began quick-freezing experiments there, and once said that his contribution was to take Eskimo knowledge and scientific theory and adapt them to quantity production. In 1924 he began work on his plate freezer to freeze food in small packages suitable for retailing. In 1929 the Postum Corporation, now General Foods, bought his company for twenty-two million dollars and divided his name into the now familiar trademark Birds Eye. Birdseye often likened the frozen food industry to a small infant: plenty of noise at one end and an absolute lack of control at the other. He died in New York on 7th October 1956.

Finally, a few words about the history of canned foods, or **Canning** as Sir Joseph Banks, at the time president of the Royal Society, called them, 'Embalmed provisions'.

There are cookery books of the seventeenth and eighteenth centuries which mention the preservation of fruit by bottling. The fruit is to be placed in loosely-corked bottles, and these set up to the neck in cold water. Thereafter the water should be heated to boiling point and then cooled. The corks are then to be beaten hard into the bottles and sealed with pitch.

This method probably worked well with acid fruit, because *Clostridium*, an important food poisoning organism, does not grow and produce toxin below pH 4.5. Most fruit have a pH value below that, and processing at 100°C or below is quite adequate for safe preservation.

In 1808 Thomas Saddington received a prize of five guineas from the Society of Arts for essentially the same method, and before him, Needham, Spallanzani and Scheele had independently suggested that food could be preserved by boiling and then excluding air. So bottling was well-known by 1800; but it was the Frenchman Appert who investigated the process thoroughly. Figure 21 shows his picture on a French postage stamp of 1955. Two statements on this stamp are of interest. Appert's first name is given as Nicolas. But in the catalogues of both the British Library and the Bibliothèque Nationale, the name of the author of his famous book[13] is entered as: APPERT (Charles); while in the book itself his signature is reproduced simply as 'Appert'.

The second point of interest regarding the stamp is his date of birth: 1749. His death certificate states: 'Died on 1st June 1841 at Massy, Nicolas Appert, born at Chalons (Marne) son of the couple Claude Appert and Marie Huet.

He was the widower of Elizabeth Benoist. He died at the age of 91.'

However, the birth register at Chalons refers to a Nicolas Appert born on 23rd October 1752 to the wool comber Jean Appert and his wife Marie Bonvalet. Therefore, neither the date nor the name of his father or mother match. The occupation of his alleged father is also incorrect. 'Our' Appert's father was a wine merchant and not a wool comber.

So, what is known about Appert? He began his career by corking bottles in his father's wine cellars in the Champagne. Later he was employed in the kitchens of the Duke Christian 4th of Deux-Ponts. He then held various commercial posts until about 1780, when he started his own confectionery shop in Paris. He left the shop in 1794 to concentrate entirely on his research and was made a local government official at Ivry-sur-Seine in 1795. In 1804 he obtained financial backing and built a small factory at Massy with about fifty employees. In 1810 he was awarded Fr. 12,000 on condition that his method of preservation be made public. So in the same year he

124

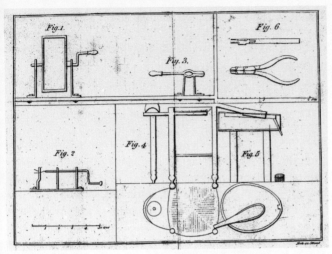

**22.**
Appert's apparatus
from an illustration in
his book.

published his famous book: *L'Art de Conserver pendant
plusiers Années toutes les Substances Animales et Végétales.*

Six thousand copies were printed, and the pharmacist
Mohr (incidentally the inventor of the Mohr clip) translated
the book into German. The first English translation
appeared in 1811. Appert claimed that his process allowed
produce to be kept from one season to another, was of
incalculable benefit both to the navy in preventing scurvy,
and to the French wine growers in preserving grape syrup
without the use of sugar. His apparatus is shown in Figure
22.

The preservation of peas gives an example of his process.
The peas were placed into sturdy glass bottles which were
then knocked on a stool to compact the content. The stool
had been covered with leather and stuffed with hay. Corks
were then inserted into the bottles and beaten into place
with a wooden bat. Next the corks were tied with wire and
covered with a seal of quicklime and cheese which remained
stable on heating. The bottles were then placed into canvas
bags so that it was easier to pick up the pieces if they

exploded. They were then heated in a water bath. After cooling to room temperature the corks were covered with rosin, a natural resin, and the seals and containers inspected.

Altogether Appert bottled anything he could get his hands on: meat and fish, fruit and vegetables, milk, butter and eggs, beer and wine, coffee and tea, roasted chestnuts and cough mixture. In 1814 his factory was destroyed by the allies in the Napoleonic wars, and he had to sell his land to repay the mortgage. He must have been over sixty-five by then, but he carried on gamely. He moved once more into new premises and continued with some of his old equipment. By 1824 he was using Papin's digesters (autoclaves) instead of a water bath, and had introduced soldered metal cans. Little is known about Appert's later years. Apparently he left his business to his nephew, and retired on a small state pension to a little house in Massy. Eventually he died so poor that he had to be buried in a pauper's grave.

It is generally assumed that metal cans were invented in England in 1810, the same year in which Appert's book appeared. Augustus de Heine patented iron cans on 26th February and Peter Durand tinned ones on 25th August 1810. However, suitable metal containers were already being made at the Royal Laboratory in Greenwich c. 1750. One drawing of a set of ten depicting the various activities at the laboratory show how tin cases for grapeshot were made from sheet metal and their lids soldered on.[14]

Brian Donkin bought Durand's patent for £1000, and in 1813 Hall and Donkin sold cans of meat from their iron works in Dartford. The Brian Donkin Co. Ltd., celebrated their 150th jubilee in 1953. There is a letter of Donkins dated 30th June 1817 in which he writes that he had sold £3000 of canned meat in the previous six months.

At first the can lid was simply soldered on. In 1819 Captain Sir Edward Parry sailed on his first voyage of discovery of the North-west passage and took some of the

**23.**
A 4 lb can of roasted
veal manufactured by
Donkin and Gamble,
part of the stores of
HMS Hekla taken to
the Arctic by Captain
Parry in 1824. The
filler hole is visible in
front of the carrier
ring.

cans of meat along with him. Two of these early cans
eventually ended up in museums and were opened and
analysed in 1938, after 114 years.[15] There was no rancidity
and, strangely, the vitamin D had survived. Vitamin B was
analysed by Dr Magnus Pyke (who later wrote the first
*Manual of Nutrition*,[16] and became a television personality).

**24.**
Right: Three piece soldered tinplate can shown in fig. 23 (inset: half-inch flange and cap). Contents: 4 lbs: 1824. Left: Two piece drawn aluminium can with ring-pull (inset: double seam). Contents: 330 ml: 1989.

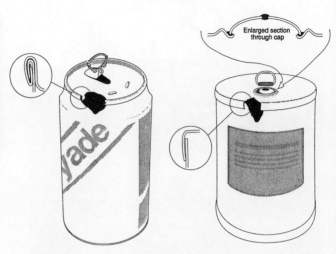

In 1823 the vent hole cover was invented and until *c.* 1900 all cans were filled through a 'stud hole' (Figures 23 and 24) so the food had to be cut up small, and amongst sailors this led tinned meat to become known as 'Fanny Adams'. Miss Adams had been a Portsmouth prostitute who was murdered and her body dismembered during the early part of the nineteenth century. After the can had been filled and sterilised a circular piece of tin was soldered on (Figure 24). A cannery of the mid-nineteenth century is shown in Figure 25. In 1897 Charles Ams patented the sealing compound and after 1900 sealing machines to make flanges were used much as they are today.

Testing of the early cans consisted of leaving them for one month at 100°F. If they did not burst they would then last for many years. This was not a very sound method because *Clostridium* type E does not produce gas, which would bulge out the can; and it would not therefore have been recognised. The use of thermocouples to measure heat transfer inside cans is described in the first volume of the journal *Food Technology* of 1931 from the Camden Research Station.[17]

128

**25.**
Soldering tin canisters, *ca.*1850. Half-cooked meat was placed in the can with some liquid, the lid was soldered on, and the whole sterilised for 30 minutes in salt solution. The latter raised the boiling-point.

Modern canning plants still employ separate retorts similar to the Papin digester which had been used by Appert (Figure 26). If a very high throughput is required, as is the case with, e.g., pet foods, a hydrostatic steriliser is used. Here the required pressure is provided by a high column of water. Such a plant has a capacity of 400 cans per minute or 24,000 cans per hour (Figure 27).

**Atomic radiation**

X-rays were discovered in 1895 and radioactive breakdown of atoms in 1896. Ionising radiation consists of $\alpha$, $\beta$ and $\delta$ rays where the first two are particulate, and the third, $\delta$ - radiation, is electromagnetic. In the early part of the twentieth century their lethal effect on micro-organisms was demonstrated, and in 1930 O. Wüst patented a method of preserving food in sealed containers by X-rays. (Fr. Pat. 701,302). The 1930–40s saw the development of large X-ray and $\beta$ beam generators, and in 1943 hamburgers were

**26.**
Battery of retorts for can sterilisation. Note overhead rails to carry the baskets to the retorts. (By courtesy of M & P (Engineering) Ltd.)

irradiated at MIT (Massachussetts Institute of Technology).

Since 1980 several countries permit the irradiation of food, for example, Bulgaria, Canada, France, Holland, Hungary and the USSR. Britain has recently allowed the sale of irradiated food. Figure 28 shows a modern irradiation plant. Food packed on palletts circulates around a heavily shielded core of Cobalt 60.

At the irradiation levels permitted, there appears to be no danger to health. There is some damage to certain nutrients, but no more than with other methods of preservation. However, at the doses required for sterilisation, there are significant changes in the product, and therefore, at present, irradiation cannot be seen as an alternative to canning.

**Notes and References**

1. J. C. Leuchs, *Lehre der Aufbewahrung und Erhaltung aller Körper* (Nuremberg, 1820).
2. G. Campbell-Platt, *Fermented Foods of the World: a Dictionary and Guide* (London, 1987).
3. H. G. Muller, *Introduction to Tropical Food Science* (Cambridge, 1988).

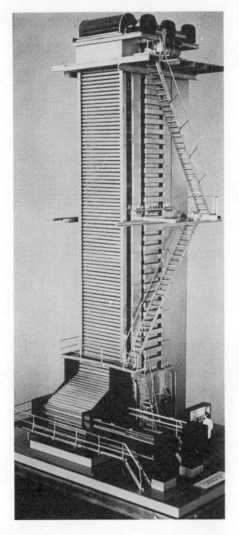

**27.**
The hydrostat
steriliser. In this
model, note the scale
from the figure of the
man who appears at
bottom right. (By
courtesy of M & P
(Engineering) Ltd.)

4.  V. Weelock, 'Public perception of food safety', *J. Roy. Soc. Health*, 108 (1988), pp. 130–1.
5.  *The Goodman of Paris, c. 1393*, ed. E. Power (London, 1928) quoted in: C. A. Wilson, *Food and Drink in Britain* (London, 1973).

**28.**
Automatic pallet
irradiation. (By
courtesy of A E C L
Irradiation Division.)

**PALLET IRRADIATOR-AUTOMATIC**

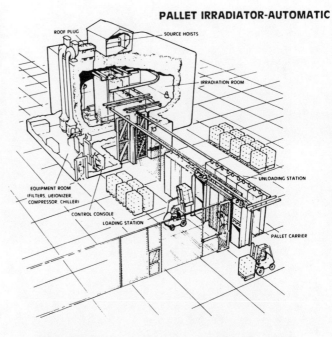

6.  H. G. Muller & G. Tobin, *Nutrition and Food Processing.* (London, 1980).
7.  C. J. Bradish, C. M. Brain & A. S. McFarlane, 'Vacuum sublimation of ice in bulk', *Nature*, 159 (1947), pp. 28–9.
8.  M. Donovan, *Domestic Economy* (London, Vol. I, 1830. Vol. II, 1837).
9.  J. C. Loudon, *An Encyclopaedia of Cottage, Farm and Villa Architecture* . . . new ed. (London, 1839), pp. 363–6.
10. W. R. Woolrich, 'History of refrigeration 1748–1968' *ASHRAE Journal* 11 (1969), pp. 31–9.
11. R. Salmon & W. Warrell, Production of cold and condensation or congelation by causing a blast of air to act on the surface of water so as to evaporate it, and then re-collecting the water and repeating the process. B.P. No. 4,331. 15 January 1819.
12. J. Black, *Experiments upon Magnesia Alba, Quicklime and other Alcaline Substances. To which is annexed, An Essay on the Cold Produced by Evaporating Fluids and some other Means of Producing Cold* by W. Cullen, Professor of Medicine in the University of Edinburgh (Edinburgh, 1782).
13. Appert: *Le livre de Tous les Menages, ou l'Art de Conserver pendant plusiers Années toutes les Substances Animales et Végétales* (Paris, 1810).

*Industrial food preservation*

14.  C. Fox, *Londoners* (London, 1987).
15.  Anon. *Historic Tinned Foods*. Publication Number 85.
     International Tin Research and Development Council, 1939.
16.  Ministry of Agriculture, Fisheries and Food: *Manual of Nutrition*
     (London, 1945).
17.  J. W. Black, 'The scientific basis of food preservation by heat',
     *Food Technology* 1 (1931), pp. 60-2.

# 6.

## *Nineteenth- and Twentieth-Century Trends in Food Preserving: Frugality, Nutrition or Luxury*

LYNETTE HUNTER

To set the story in a context: before the easy-to-purchase and relatively cheap food supplies of the second half of the nineteenth century, skills in the preservation of food were essential to survival. Such skills were, arguably, the most important part of the domestic economy: conserving and preserving and storing the fruits, vegetables and meats from a period of harvest or slaughter through a period of scarcity. The pattern of feast or famine was after all dependent upon unavoidable seasonal constraint on the supply of food and on the economic ability to obtain it. Underlying all the evidence from surviving printed books, the basic necessities of sustenance depended upon a good knowledge of how to store foods and how to dry them, neither method involving any additional expenditure, and then upon salting, and to a smaller extent potting. Preserving with sugar and alcohol was, for centuries, too costly for general domestic use, and the use of vinegar, particularly in pickles and relishes, was largely for making condiments rather than preserving foods.

Knowledge of preserving techniques was so important that it must have been part of the basic training of most people up until the early nineteenth century at least, and was probably orally transmitted. In choosing to look at preserving and changing attitudes toward it from the evidence of printed books, I am taking a particular perspective that works under a number of constraints

134

which can be touched upon by trying to respond to the question: why did people see a need to write down these accounts rather than simply transmit them orally? One reason may have been the need to respond to entirely new social events, such as the shift from a largely rural to a concentrated urban population, or to the adulteration of foodstuffs, or the effect of changes in architecture. Another reason was the need to inform people about contemporary discoveries of new techniques and preserving agents. A third and highly problematic reason must have been the need to adapt these essential skills to the changing activities of men and women in the household, adapt them from the more integrated domestic scene of pre-1600 to the separate and relatively isolated work of the housewife, the housekeeper and the servant.[1]

Until the early nineteenth century each of these reasons, and they are only a selected few, uses the print medium to tell a specifically middle-class audience about something new, and in this sense looking at evidence from printed books yields an atypical picture of what was happening even for the middle classes. At the same time these books do indicate a considerable amount about the construction of domestic social activity in the middle classes from the Renaissance to the coming of industrialisation. Where the picture becomes far more complicated is during the nineteenth and twentieth centuries when the print medium reaches out to a vastly enlarged audience, and we begin to see preserving skills presented in radically different ways. The main part of this discussion will explore the reasons behind the dearth of preserving information in most domestic cookery books from the 1830s, and its re-introduction into some groups of books from the 1880s. The chapter suggests that skills which had been necessary to survival because they ensured a supply of food, whether to the agrarian or the new family domestic economy, were, for a number of reasons, simply made redundant in the early nineteenth century. What becomes of interest is why

135

people then chose to reintroduce these skills and what reasons they had for doing so.

The books that survive from the sixteenth to early nineteenth centuries are, for the most part, substantial cared-for products that represent a relatively affluent readership. Simply due to the way books were produced during this period,[2] much ephemeral writing aimed at labouring people has not survived, and we have few examples to indicate what might have been the concerns of such an audience. Of the extant books concerning food from the sixteenth to mid-seventeenth centuries, most address the courtly lady or the gentlewoman emerging from the newly landed gentry;[3] and most present preserving skills as an important domestic responsibility with one or two writers treating the field, superficially at least, as a lady-like hobby.[4] The earliest cookery books were concerned with sugar cookery, much of it directed to the preserving and conserving qualities of this relatively new foodstuff which was suddenly coming into Europe in large quantities.[5] Other aspects of preserving were primarily to do with vinegars, and these sections were often combined into books with sections on medicine or cosmetics and brewing. By the 1630s, sections on preserving were increasingly often included in books about cookery, although the two sections were kept quite separate. Indeed one of the reasons preserving was considered a suitable activity for an aristocratic lady may well have been its separation from mundane cookery, as well as the prestige it carried with it of a knowledge essential to housekeeping. Partly, one suspects, in an attempt to imitate what was thought to be the life-style of aristocratic women, several late seventeenth and early eighteenth century books like *The Accomplish'd Female Instructor* (1704) aim to teach conduct, preserving, conserving, household receipts and medicines but not cookery.

After the Commonwealth period and particularly after 1695,[6] books on food were aimed more and more at burgeoning middle-classes. The books that survive indicate that an understanding of preserving skills was still considered essential to the activity of the household.[7] It was the fundamental knowledge upon which planning ahead, budgeting and responsible household management were founded. But the kind of household in question, and particularly the work of women within it, was becoming quite different from that of the late Renaissance. An example of how the household was changing can be gained from a comparison of Gervase Markham's *Country Contentments* (1615) with Eliza Smith's *The Complete Housewife* (1727). Markham delineates the duties that fall to the woman of a household but also outlines their interconnection with the whole range of domestic responsibilities. Furthermore, it is clear that Markham's woman of the household would not have been working alone. In contrast, Eliza Smith concentrated on preserving, cookery and brewing as specifically the housewife's or gentlewoman's province, and includes seasonal bills of fare, table-settings and medical recipes. It is not totally clear, but the impression is given that Smith's housewife is not working with a group of people although she may have had servants. Markham's woman of the house is working within a rural economy, firmly seasonal, and she survives into the eighteenth century, mainly in the form of the housekeeper to large landed houses (H. Glasse) and partly in the new profession of innkeeper (E. Raffald). Smith's housewife, still aware of the seasons, is an urban creature dependent upon street markets, whose successors become less and less gentlewomen and more plain housewives to whom preserving skills are, as in Penelope Bradshaw's *Family Companion* (1750) or Susannah Carter's *The Frugal Housewife* (1765) or E. Spencer's *The Modern Cook; and Frugal Housewife's Complete Guide* (1782), a matter of domestic management and frugal housekeeping.

Until the early nineteenth century nearly all women would have had to know something about preserving food.

137

Apart from alerting women to the professions of house-keeper and innkeeper and popularising individual writers, the main reason for printed books on the topic must lie partly in the changing social structure of the middle-class domestic household, which gradually placed all the responsibility for these skills onto the single housewife – although she may have directed servants to help her – and partly in the market-based economy which the housewife had to learn to use frugally.[8] Later in the eighteenth century a better understanding about the principles of preserving food, with a new technology applying the understanding and with commercial outlets exploiting the product, fundamentally undermined the need for such skills in a domestic setting aimed at frugality and in doing so fundamentally altered the activity of the housewife: she no longer preserves but buys, she no longer produces for herself but consumes products made for her. More than this, activities that would have occupied a large part of domestic budgeting and household management no longer needed to be carried out. In order to grasp the far-reaching effects of changes in the technology of preserving I would like to summarise some background dealt with in greater detail elsewhere in this book.

Preserving techniques in Britain until the early nineteenth century, in descending importance to the majority and in ascending cost, included drying, salting, potting, vinegar-pickling, sugar-bottling or candying, and conserving in alcohol. As with all preserving techniques, they depend either on the addition of a preservative or upon the deprivation of the rotting agent which is usually either moisture, air or heat. Sometimes the former affects the latter. The main aim of each technique was to keep the foodstuff edible until such time as it was to be eaten, although the process would have produced flavours and textures which came to be appreciated for themselves. The most widely written-about techniques in these early books for the middle-classes discuss the use of salt and sugar.

The story of nineteenth century preserving technology is mainly about how the use of sugar in bottling came to be superseded by canning, and the use of salt in dry-salting, brining and pickling came to be superseded also by canning but more importantly by refrigeration.

In the late medieval period sugar was a very expensive product. It was soon recognised that it could be made to go further by diluting it with water into a syrup. Although this lessened its preserving qualities, the bottles that held the syrup served another function by excluding air. The exclusion of air was an important principle that interested many early scientists such as Robert Boyle,[9] and people who wrote books with sections on preserving often implied and sometimes explained that bottling was the main technique allowing for economising on sugar.[10] Yet even in the eighteenth century there was an awareness of further complexities, and writers advise on the preference for narrow-necked jars and warn their readers not to put their fingers, or utensils that have been used for other foods on the table, into jars of preserves.[11] Until the late eighteenth century, most recipes concentrate on excluding air from coming in: there are elaborate combinations of lids, paper, brandy-paper, leather, bladder, cork, cork and resin – and excluding materials – fat (preferably mutton because of its low setting point), oil, or juice (for example lemon). But it was gradually recognised, particularly following Priestley's work with oxygen in the 1760s, that another problem was the 'air' already in the jar, in the very mixture to be preserved. This problem was referred to as 'oxidation' and was the main concern of the next advance in technology.

Due to a sugar shortage during the Napoleonic Wars, the post-revolutionary government established a prize to encourage new work on the preservation of food in bottles. In 1808 Saddington proposed, to the English Society for Arts, the boiling and scalding of bottles as a solution; and in 1810 Nicolas Appert finally won the large money prize from the French government for his careful organisation of heated bottles with a champagne-type seal. The results of Appert's work were studied by the chemist Guy-Lussac, who concluded that it was the oxygen being driven out of the bottle during heating, and then prevented from re-entering, which resulted in success and the prevention of oxidation. At precisely this time, again with the practicalities of army provender in mind, Peter Durand in England took out a patent on sealing food in cans. Canned food was taken on Parry's arctic explorations in 1814–16, and came into its own during the Crimean War.[12]

By the 1830s the principles were better understood and the technology more precisely applied so that there was a reliable method for producing bottled goods, and the same could be said for canned goods by the 1850s.[13] But the products had to reach the buying household. This they did through the explosion in retail trade outlets or shops occurring in most urban centres[14] from the 1840s, and eventually all but supplanting the street markets. The products needed the shops and the shops needed the products. Markets were increasingly less central to the dominant urban economy and the housewife was urged instead into shop-bought bottled and canned goods by a growing advertising industry based on the packaging of the goods.[15] Evidence that the housewife responded does seem to be provided by the cookery books of the early nineteenth century. Elizabeth Raffald's *The Experienced English House-keeper* which was published several times between 1769 and 1796, has a large and consistent section on preserving. In contrast, an equally popular nineteenth-century book, *A New System of Domestic Cookery* (second edition, 1807) by Maria Eliza Rundell, includes a large number of preserving recipes in the early edition of 1807, but by 1819 there are far fewer. Some recipes were shifted to a section specifically on sweetmeats. Also of possible significance, whereas the writer/editor of the 1807 edition explicitly stated at the start of the sweetmeat section that these recipes were less important for private families since such things could be bought at far less expense than they could be made, the identical statement is transposed to the preserving section in the edition of 1819.[16]

By the middle of the nineteenth century, so few cookery books contain a substantial section on preserving that the exceptions to this rule are particularly informative. In Eliza Acton's *Modern Cookery* of 1845 there are detailed instructions for preserving fruit, but we have to remember that this is the same Acton who was a working journalist, concerned with issue of public welfare, and who was to write *The English Bread Book* (1857), specifically to address the problem of the adulteration of shop-bought bread by encouraging people to make their own. By the 1868 edition of *Modern Cookery*, Acton feels the need to make the same intentions clear for her section on preserving and scathingly criticises the 'unwholesome [preserved] fruit vended and consumed in very large quantities' by the shop-buying public.[17] Acton's stress on the 'wholesome' is a significant precursor of the direction that preserving recipes will take when they re-enter cookery books at the end of the nineteenth century. No longer can the housewife claim to be frugal when she uses preserving skills, but she can claim to produce more nutritious and healthy food. The same argument, however, did not apply to salting.

Techniques of preserving that used salt were far more widespread than those using the more expensive sugar, and much older in cultural practice.[18] Although eggs and some vegetables, particularly green beans,[19] were salted, the main foodstuff preserved in this way was meat.[20] Beef cattle in particular were slaughtered wholesale in the autumn because there was rarely enough hay to keep them through the winter, so the meat had to be preserved. Brining and dry-salting must have been such a central part of general life that it is not surprising that there are few recipes in the early cookery books, despite the fact that with the imposition of taxes on salt from 1785 to 1825, frugality with salt must have been important.[21] By the end of the eighteenth century, most books included some recipes, for example there is almost always one for Westphalia ham and salt beef, and from the early nineteenth century there is an increasing number of recipes for foreign salted foods like polonis and salamis, presumably in response to wider continental travel of private families. But these recipes, too, disappear from most domestic cookery books after the mid-century, only surfacing in a few trade receipt books for professional shop-keepers like James Robinson's *The Whole Art of Curing, Pickling and Preserving* (1847). This work is addressed to the trades, particularly the fishmongers, but includes (unacknowledged) many of Rundell's recipes: the line between commercial and domestic preserving was not yet clearly drawn.[22]

It appears that the main reason that salting recipes fade from cookery books, apart of course from the advent of the can, is the introduction both of ice-cooled and of refrigerated boxes during the 1830s. The use of cold to preserve food had fascinated the English from Bacon's experiments in 1626,[23] to Pepys' amazed discussion in the 1670s on the frozen Baltic chickens, to the later 1799 discovery of the frozen mammoths in Russia. Since the Renaissance, several great country houses in Britain had had ice-houses,[24] but until Rundell's advice in 1807 on unfreezing food slowly, there were few remarks in general domestic books.[25] From the early 1800s the trade in ice grew from the first imports from Norway in 1822, to the artificial production of ice in the 1860s. At the same time Jacob Perkins, an American engineer working in Britain, developed the ice-cooled refrigerator and produced it for sale between 1835 and 1870.[26] From the 1860s meat was available in cans, and from the 1880s cheap imports from Australia and New Zealand were being imported in cans and by refrigerated ships.

A secondary reason for the loss of salting recipes was a growing concern with the nutritional value of preserved foods. Michael Donovan, that centre of sense, comments that 'The object is . . . to preserve, as much as possible, the nutritiousness of food and its salubrity, and to prevent its doing actual injury to health . . .' (p. 243). Just as the French army was concerned with dependable food supply during the Napoleonic Wars, so the British army launched intensive study into methods of food preserving during the 1840s and 1850s leading up to the Crimean War. *Food and its Adulterations* compiled by A. Hill Halsall in 1855 lists a series of tests conducted by and for the army in ways of keeping meat without salting it: not only canning and drying but also smoking, packing in tin foil, vacuum-packing and producing extracts of vegetables and meat.[27] In 1859 Beeton states that the action of salt on meat decreases its nutritive value, and by 1870 William Tegetmeier is advising against the consumption of much if any salted meat.[28] There is some evidence that American trends in health foods also began to have some influence on British attitudes toward eating at the end of the nineteenth century. Russell Trall's *The New Hydropathic Cookbook*, published in England from 1883, cites salt meat as the prime example of bad food. Also during this period there was the vigorous commercial marketing of Liebig's 'Extract of Meat' for domestic use, by the LEMCO organisation whose advertising suggested that salting meat was deleterious to health. Indeed, apart from one or two recipes apparently included to satisfy those who craved the taste of salted meat, and a brief resurgence from 1918 to the year 1925 (when the Public Health Preservation in Food Act actively promoted domestic refrigeration), only a few recipes for salting meat occur in British cookery books until Jane Grigson's *Charcuterie* of 1967.[29]

Some of this account may help us partly to understand the dearth of preserving recipes in domestic cookery books from the 1830s to the 1880s. What is more difficult to assess is why any such recipes should have reappeared at all. From the 1850s onward, the audience for printed cookery books expanded considerably,[30] and exploded during the 1870s and 80s on the back of a proliferating periodical publishing industry, which was creating markets and responding to the demands for a wide range of general topics accessible to the reading publics that were defined in the aftermath of the Education Acts of 1867 and 1870. At the same time cookery books continued their progress into specialised genres, and focused not only on narrower topics but also on class divisions. Alexis Soyer's *The Gastronomic Regenerator* (upper-class, recherche dishes), *The Modern Housewife* (middle-class) and *Shilling Cookery* (artisan) is but one example of a specifically class-orientated approach common to many writers of the mid-century.[31] But for high or low, rich or poor, few of these books contained advice on preserving although several contained advice on how to use canned goods, for instance Emily de Vere Matthew on *Tinned Meats* (1887), and Jane Panton's *From Kitchen to Garret* (1888) which advised on the use of cheap canned and frozen New Zealand meat. One exception which *may* indicate a group of 'lost' books is the publication from the Labourer's Friend Society *A Second Series of Useful Hints for Labourers* (London, 1840) aimed at the artisan with an allottment[32] and containing advice on how to salt your pig.[33]

However, in the explosion of the 1870s and 1880s a distinct pattern emerges: books for working-class women do not contain recipes for preserving while those for middle-class women, and slightly later also for wives of artisans, do. *The Official Handbook for the Training School for Cookery*, published from 1888 for many years, contains recipes for using canned meat, one recipe for pickling meat and one for pickling cabbage. The foremost reason for the lack of preserving recipes is economic. The wider ranging household management and planning requirements of preserving of any kind imply having the time to do it, the money to buy ingredients in bulk as well as preserving agents and equipment, as well as, usually, a

144

source of heat and always space for storage. Most of the urban working-class population would not have had easy access to all, or indeed any of these requirements. The very concept of there being periods of plenty during which people save up against periods of famine is not part of an industrial working pattern. Neither the school text-books written for this audience nor the more general books of advice to these housewives, consider preserving as an important skill. Indeed W. Tegetmeier's *A Manual of Domestic Economy* (1870) account of working-class diet assumes that any fruit and vegetables are a luxury to this class, let alone being available in quantities enough to preserve. And fifty years later C. H. Senn's *Popular Cookery* of 1920 assumes that its readers buy in any preserved foods they need from shops – although his *Practical Gastronomy* (1892) for the middle-class house-wife contains a range of recipes for conserves and pickles. Contrary to some current speculations, there is growing evidence not only from the cookery books but also from recent research in social history, that cans and can-openers were accessible to and used by the working-class population of the late nineteenth century.[34]

Unlike schools for working-class girls, middle-class schools did not teach cookery, so the text-books on general food preparation and management for these readers were usually written for specific Cookery Schools. Apart from these books this audience was also addressed by practical household management books which assumed that the housewife had at least one servant, by textbooks written for women attending the National Training Schools of Cookery in order to teach domestic economy in schools, and by conduct or etiquette books whose purpose was to provide information about what needed to be done in your household but did not expect you to do it yourself. There are several strands offered by these books when they include recipes for preserving, but the most important is that of nutrition. To understand the influence of this strand, it is useful to look again at changes in the understanding of the principles of food preservation.

Until the early 1800s, the scientific and technological attention to preserving had focused on preventing the foods from rotting for immediate reasons of economy and frugality. Nineteenth-century scientific advances document a shift in focus away from frugality to nutrition: a move that closely parallels and must be interconnected with the same shift in the cookery books of the period, for preceding the resurgence of preserving recipes in books for a middle-class audience are the few books on vegetarianism or 'health' foods, usually beginning in the United States, directed with prophetic fervour to a more wholesome diet. These isolated books from the 1840s to the 1880s are being produced at the same time that Pasteur and Tyndall are doing their separate but related work on the effects of yeasts, moulds and bacteria on the deterioration of food.[35] Evidence that air carried not only 'oxidising' agents but also unseen organisms that rotted food, led to even more efficient systems for bottling and canning. However Britain, possibly because of its concentrated urban, industralised and shop-centred domestic economy, was slow to respond. Despite the success of George Fowler's patented bottling system during the 1890s,[36] even in 1916 the Royal Horticultural Society is complaining about the need to import good bottles from the Continent,[37] and canning was never a serious proposition for domestic preservation even in National Training School text-books,[38] although some books from the United States containing substantial instructions on canning were published here from 1890 to 1920[39] and there was certainly a domestic canning machine on the market.[40]

At the turn of the century scientific attention began to focus on the newly-discovered presence of enzymes, along with an extended understanding of fermentation processes and an appreciation of the role of vitamins in body chemistry. For food preservation, the end result of this attention was a proliferation of suggestions for preserving food with as little heat as possible. Concern for the role that enzymes played in determining the taste of food as well as concern for the delicate biochemical balance maintained at body temperatures, meant the recognition that heating foods to preserve them in bottles was destroying their nutritional and gastronomic value. One solution was a short-lived attempt to promote the pressure cooking of cans for brief time periods,[41] and another was the extensive and helpful experiment by the Royal Horticultural Society on the shortest effective heating times and lowest effective temperature for bottling which led to a classic book on bottling which has been adapted and revised for nearly a century: *Fruit Bottling*.[42] But, ironically, the primary response to the deleterious effects of heat was to consider what could be 'added' to the environment of the food to stop rotting agents getting to it while preserving its natural processes. In the balance were two processes. The first concentrated on providing a surrounding unfriendly to bacteria and moulds, and here chemical additives came into their own. In 1859 Isabella Beeton, among a few others, had advocated using alum in bottling fruit in order to increase the dependability of preserving, but from the late 1800s more and more chemicals were added for this purpose, the most common being sodium sulphite.[43] The second process to which people at that time paid increasing attention, was that these additives might not only prevent the entry of external rotting agents but might also slow down, possibly by altering it, the natural maturation of the foods themselves. It is difficult to differentiate between the two processes and the second clearly changes the nutritional value and probably also the taste of the foodstuff. Worry about exactly what these additives were doing became so widespread, as use of them became more and more ubiquitous,[43] that the government had to control them, and in 1925 published the Public Health Preservation in Food Act, which is in effect an early listing of allowable and prohibited E-numbers.[45]

The focus on the wholesome and the nutritious by scientists and technologists, was filtered out into books for a middle-class audience primarily through the text-books for training domestic economy teachers. These text-books, initially appearing in the 1870s and 1880s, claim for those who study them a serious area of learning. In most the pedagogic tone is based on the rhetoric of modern science: fact, proof, method and explanation. It has been suggested elsewhere,[46] and I think it is underwritten by these books, that domestic economy teachers were trying to define a field of academically respectable study in order to justify the serious status of their work; and since there were more obviously scientific aspects in preserving than elsewhere in cookery, it was a clear field for emphasis in their training.

The kind of book produced for these training schools, such as Catherine Buckton's *Food and Home Cookery* (London, 1879) or E. G. Mann's *Domestic Science Manuals* (London, 1899) among very many others, drew on an earlier tradition of male writers who had worked in the technical schools of the 1850s to 1870s. John Buckmaster's lectures on cookery were brought together into *Buckmaster's Cookery* (London, 1874) and William Mattieu Williams produced *The Chemistry of Cookery* (London, 1885). Both writers were widely influential, particularly Buckmaster who lectured at the National Training School for Cookery in London, and both focused on science as the basis for domestic cookery, Williams stating that

> The kitchen is a chemical laboratory in which are conducted a number of chemical processes by which our food is converted from its crude state to a condition more suitable for digestion and nutrition, and made more agreeable to the palate (p. 4).

148

In turn, Buckton and her colleagues in their text-books for training teachers, are concerned to discuss oxidation, fermentation, fibres, yeasts, moulds, bacteria, pasteurisation, sterilisation and so on; and they do so largely in the context of the preservation of wholesome and nutritious food.

When the students of the training schools went on to write domestic cookery books of their own at the turn of the century, as many of them did, preserving once more found a place, again firmly in terms of nutrition and wholesomeness. For example there is M. Fairclough's *The Ideal Cookery Book*, written for her cookery school, and containing a large section on preserving. The domestic reader had books such as *The Housewife's Cookery Book* published in 1920 but in effect an update of *Warne's Model Cookery* from 1871, which begins with the claim that 'The science of cookery is a knowledge of the choice of food and food materials, for just as an engine requires food to enable it to work, so the body requires certain foodstuffs to keep it in working order' (p. 1), yet continues much as the 1871 edition, but with the addition of a substantial section on bottling.

Less pretentious were the many specialised books focusing on preserves such as Helen Souter's *Aunt Kate's Jams and Jellies Book* (1910) or Rose Brown's *Pastry and Preserves* (1906) or S. Beaty Pownall's *Queen Cookery: Pickles and Preserves* (1908). These writers also contributed to a small group of books aimed at teaching the newly-impoverished genteel lady how to make delicacies that one could no longer afford to buy: an interesting index to the fact that economy could be reintroduced as an element. Furthermore, they also produced a well-defined but still limited group of books aimed at the upper-middle class lady with time on her hands and searching for something to do. Just as this lady was usually expected to be able to produce at least one meal on her own, a star turn, for the delight of her husband, she could also turn to the making of preserves

149

as a delicate hobby. Like the newly-emerging monied woman of the early seventeenth century to whom she was occasionally compared,[47] the late nineteenth-century lady could not be involved in mundane cookery but could take on the role of producing elegant gifts, acting the Lady Bountiful.

These Lady Bountiful books formed a curious partnership with the other main promoter of new preserving skills: the Royal Horticultural Society. Possibly due to the Allotment Act of 1887 which made it legally necessary for all local authorities to provide allotments, large numbers of people were growing their own vegetables and fruits, and from 1910 the Royal Horticultural Society was awarding prizes and medals for preserved fruits and vegetables.[48] In 1916 the society published Wilks' *Fruit-Bottling*, its flagship guide to preserving. However, the response from individual members of the Horticultural Society began earlier with for example the series of articles by May Crooke in the 1905 *Farm and Garden* on the small-holdings commission, or the Stoney's *A Simple Method for Bottling Fruit at Home* (1910) or Edith Bradley's *The Book of Fruit Bottling* (1907). This last contains an introduction by Wilks in which he comments that fruit bottling had gone downhill from the 1840s when he was a boy to its nadir in 1885, when 'I doubt whether there were a dozen ladies in the land who did their own bottling and preserving' (p. x). These books arrived just in time to lay a basis for response to the demands of World War I. Ernest Oldmeadow straightforwardly entitles his contribution: *Home Cookery in War-Time* (1915), and resuscitates many eighteenth-century preserving methods such as the use of mutton fat to seal jars, in an attempt at economy. While the Great War did remind people that domestic preserving could save money, the stress was still on health. Louise Andrea's *Home Bottling Drying and Preserving* (1920) emphasises the conservation of 'nutritive value' and the 'wholesome', but in the light of war-time experience she proclaims 'Empty jars can be put to splendid use; if allowed to remain empty they are voiceless but eloquent reproaches' (p. 10); indeed 'Empty jars are slackers' (p. 18). By the end of the war Bristol University had established a Fruit and Vegetable Preservation Research Station.[49]

After the war there was another wave of books specifically on preserves and of general books containing substantial sections on preserves. Among the former are the Banks's *Fruit and Vegetable Bottling* (1928), the Royal Horticultural Society's update on Wilks' *Fruit-Bottling*, and the closely related *Domestic Preservation of Fruit and Vegetables* (1929), edited by M. L. Adams for the Ministry of Agriculture. Among the latter are found the Good Housekeeping Institute's newly influential guides. The Good Housekeeping Institute's director, D. Cottington Taylor, also published *Frigidaire Recipes* which is by and large cooking with refrigerated foods in 1930, and by 1938 the Canned Foods Advisory Bureau employed Janet Bond to write *Janet Bond's Book: A Practical Guide to the Use of Canned Foods*, in which she claims that canned goods not only preserve more vitamins than domestic preserving, but have also arrested the decline in fruit culture, freed women from the kitchen into careers and acted as the guardian of the Nation's Health. But 1939 and World War II shifted the emphasis firmly back on to preserving within the home and the 1940s saw a whole series of guides to effective methods, led by Crang and Mason's revision of Adams' book, for the Ministry of Agriculture, under the same title *Domestic Preservation of Fruit and Vegetables* (1942). The book begins resolutely on the first page saying that:

> the object of preservation is to take food at its point
> of maximum palatability and nutritive value and
> keep it at this stage . . . a study of these changes has
> shown that they are due partly to the action of
> enzymes in the food, partly to the growth of micro-
> organisms in contaminating them.

151

It proceeds with instructions for jams, jellies, marmalade, cheeses and butters, bottling, canning, deep-freezing, chemicals, syrups, candying, preserving vegetables, vinegars, pickles, chutneys, sauces, drying, salting beans and storing. Crang and Mason's work, apart from the sections on deep freezing, could have been written before World War I, but it includes a rather different audience, the working class, in its address.

Most of these books on preserving from the 1880s to the 1940s were resolutely directed towards a middle- and upper-middle class audience, and the class specificity raises a difficult problem. Ever since domestic preserving as an essential for survival was superseded by shops and their cheap goods, it had occupied a tenuous place in cookery books. Exactly because it moved out of the mundane, or those things essential for everyday survival, it had nothing to fall back on to prove its necessity or relevance. Preserving, while attempts were being made to reclaim it in terms of nutrition, became fundamentally superfluous to daily needs. In a curious way the situation focuses on the fact that during the nineteenth century preserving in any but the most basic sense was beyond the poor, and then the working-classes: they were too impoverished to practice frugality and thereafter too impoverished to practice nutrition. It is ironic that while the Napoleonic and Crimean Wars precipitated the processes of domestic preserving out of women's hands, World War I and particularly World War II, partially put it back. The events related to these two twentieth-century wars also broadened the constituency for preserving by changing food supply routes, by making preserving once again essential to survival; and, possibly most importantly, because there had been a radical break in the oral history of preserving techniques, from say 1830 or 1840 to 1910, the surge of printed book instructions at the turn of the century were not just addressed to a privileged audience but to a much wider range of reader. An introduction to the basics went hand in hand with an introduction to condiments, relishes and conserves that were not strictly essential. General cookery books from the immediate post-1939 period invariably contain a section on preserving techniques, although these largely diminish to conserves and pickles by the end of the 50s.

Why do people continue to preserve on any scale? This is an extremely difficult question to answer. After all we do not technically need to do so for survival or nutrition, and there are many cheerful commercially-produced gift bottles around. For certain generations, in which I would include my own, there is a nostalgic remembrance of childhood post-war rationing days when it *was* necessary to bottle and jam, to harvest in plenty, to put up against want and to waste not: then as now it was often a communal and social activity. For some, there is the confidence of knowing exactly what has gone into the foodstuff: home preserving is the only sure way of evading major additives and of controlling sugar content, and so on. For many, there is the delight in the activity of cooking and in the beauty of the product, neither of which is strictly necessary. Possibly for most people preserving has become a kind of signature. Making our own preserves, conserves and pickles allows us to vary the flavour and taste of a recipe that is frequently traditional, and to recognise quite precisely how the network of food distribution and supply, quality and quantity, changes from year to year. The products are also often communally distributed, so that every year you wait with anticipation for one friend's pickle and with dread for another's jam; they are the staple of countless school sales and fund-raising fairs. Preserving brings the general domestic cook closer to the subtleties of cooking than our mundane cooking normally allows, and in our culture it is looked upon primarily as a leisure activity. How long it will remain so is unclear.

**Notes and References**

1. This shift is attested to by the surge of domestic books directed at the private housewife from the late seventeenth into the eighteenth centuries, many of which are concerned with the way that the household needs to be organised in a private dwelling and overseen by just one person: the wife. The shift is looked at briefly by A. Oakley *Housewife* (London, 1974) pp. 1–59, and the margin that it shares with conduct books is glanced at by N. Armstrong *Desire and Domestic Fiction: a Political History of the Novel* (Oxford, 1987).

2. For an account of provincial printing of cookery books see L. Hunter 'Printing in the Pennines' in *Traditional Food East and West of the Pennines*, ed. C. A. Wilson (Edinburgh, 1991).

3. I am omitting reference to books on the topic addressed to male readers, mainly because those that do exist are not primarily addressed to necessary household skills but to science, horticulture and later on to commercial production.

4. See H. Platt (London, 1605) discussed in L. Hunter 'Sweet Secrets' in *Banquetting Stuffe* ed. C. Wilson (Edinburgh, 1991).

5. See 'Sweet Secrets' as above.

6. In 1695 the Licensing Act was allowed to lapse and printing presses began to spring up all over England. Possibly because they had to serve the immediate interests of their local community many printers and booksellers moved swiftly into the field of domestic and conduct books.

7. See V. MacLean *A Catalogue of Household and Cookery Books 1701–1800* (London, 1979).

8. N. Armstrong in *Desire and Domestic Fiction* cited above argues that the ideology constructed for women during the late seventeenth and the eighteenth centuries defined the middle-class for England in terms of women decades before the male middle class began to organise itself on a private property-owning economy.

    An important aspect of the construction of middle-class ideology was the responsibility that devolved onto women of both the labouring and more especially the newly-monied classes of working out how to cope with the new economic structures of household management brought by the isolated families that resulted from aping the aristocratic 'houses'. 'Frugality' was necessary because a family had to live discreetly within one private income. The men who earned that income had little idea of how it could be used to maintain their discreet family, but household management was the largest if not the only necessary expenditure from it and women were left with the task of working out how to employ it. Knowledge of preserving was fundamental to this frugality.

9. M. Donovan *The Cabinet of Useful Arts, Domestic Economy* Vol. II (London, 1837), p. 222.

10. R. Bradley *The Country Housewife and Lady's Director, I*, 6th ed.

(London, 1736, reprinted 1980), p. 104; Or Vol. II (London, 1732), p. 74 where he suggests using apple jelly instead of sugar.

11. For example C. Millington *The Housekeeper's Domestic Library* (London, 1810 [originally 1805]), advises on keeping a separate spoon specifically for taking preserves from jars; Mrs Rundell advises putting small quantities into separate jars for daily use. See also J. Evelyn *Acetaria* (London, 1982/1691), O 8v.

12. This short history has been told many times. An account of its effect on commercial food preserving may be found in H. G. Muller's *'Industrial Food Preservation . . .'*, chapter 5. Charles (Nicolas) Appert's book, translated into English under the auspices of the East India Company is an accessible and interesting source book: *The Art of Preserving* (London, 1811).

13. By the 1850s there are large canning factories of Aberdeen and Leith with a substantial export trade according to I. Beeton *The Book of Household Management* (London, 1861), p. 299.

14. For example, A. Soyer in *The Modern Housewife* (1849) assumes that you buy beef ready-salted, and the book as a whole is partly a promotion for Crosse & Blackwell's sauces.

15. The Opie collection, now housed at The Museum of Advertising and Packaging in Gloucester, is a substantial collection of this material. The area is under-researched and needs study.

16. E. Rundell, *A New System of Domestic Cookery* (London, 1819), p. 225.

17. E. Acton, *Modern Cookery* (London, 1868), p. 494.

18. See for example M. Visser's compilation of information about salt in *Much Depends on Dinner* (Toronto, 1986); at one point he notes that the term 'corned' beef derives from the practice of covering the meat with grain-sized lumps of salt, and the 'Old Norse word *korn* which meant a grain-sized lump of anything'.

19. From John Evelyn's *Acetaria* (1699) to the Ministry of Agriculture's *Domestic Preservation* (1962), the salting of green beans is the one consistent thread in salted vegetables.

20. W. Tegetmeier asserts in *A Manual of Domestic Economy* (London, 1870), that the English have never been as enthusiastic as the Continental Europeans about salting vegetables.

21. M. Visser reports the Earl of Dundonald saying in 1785 that the taxes on salt and tobacco had led to '10,000 people . . . seized for salt smuggling, and 300 sent to the gallows for contraband trade in salt and tobacco', *Much Depends on Dinner*, p. 73.

22. J. Robinson, *The Whole Art of Curing, Pickling and Smoking* (London, 1847).

23. In 1837 M. Donovan is suggesting that Bacon even died from eating chickens that he had frozen but unfrozen too quickly. F. Blandford in *About Food Preservation* (London, 1963) says it was death from pneumonia brought on by freezing them in the first place.

24. E. David, 'Fromages, Glacés and Iced Creams', in *Petits Propos Culinaires* 2 (1979), p. 24.

25.  E. Rundell, *A New System of Domestic Cookery*, 2nd ed. (London, 1807), p. 34.

26.  See F. Blandford *About Food Preservation*, cited above, for a concise background to this history.

27.  A. Hill Halsall, *Food and its Adulterations* (London, 1855), pp. 436–47.

28.  The reference from I. Beeton is in *The Book of Household Management* (London, 1861, reprinted 1968, first published in twenty-four parts 1859–61), p. 283.

29.  H. Sarson's *Home Pickling* (London, 1940) which might have been expected to promote the use of Sarson's 'virgin vinegar' for the purpose, states that 'pickled meats are of small interest to the modern housewife' (p. 119).

30.  From the 1850s the 'taxes on knowledge', which were the taxes on advertising, postage of periodicals, paper, and rag supplies for paper, were lifted, in 1853, 1855, 1860 and 1861 respectively; this substantially lowered the cost of printing and publishing.

31.  See A. Soyer, *A Shilling Cookery for the People* (London, 1855), p. vii; and C. Francatelli, *The Modern Cook* (London, 1846) for 'private families' and his 'more economical' *Cook's Guide . . .* (London, 1861).

32.  *The Oxford Companion to Gardens* outlines a brief and helpful history of allotment-owning which grew up slowly during the nineteenth century in response to the Enclosure Acts of the late 1700s. By the 1870s Members of Parliament were standing on the 'allotment' ticket.

33.  It is difficult to ascertain from a brief survey of *The English Catalogue of Printed Books* how many of such works may have been published. They are exactly the kind of book that does not survive because it is well-used, and is not catalogued because it is not considered prestigious enough.

34.  Discoveries by Pasteur and Tyndall began to be popularised during the 1870s, *Encyclopedia Britannica* (London, 1974).

35.  A useful summary of this background can be found in O. Powell's *Successful Canning and Preserving* (London and Philadelphia, 1918).

36.  Fowler's *How to Bottle* (Maidstone, 1898) was probably instrumental to the wide range of preserving books which emerged over the next fifteen years, since it offered an early application of Appert's technology for producing bottled preserves in the home.

36.  W. Wilks, *Fruit Bottling* (London, 1916), p. 3.

37.  For example the Battersea Polytechnic textbook published from 1914 to at least 1942 contains nothing at all on canning.

39.  For example there are S. W. Dodds *Health in the Household* (New York, 1883) which had some currency in the UK during the 1890s, as did E. Witherspoon's *The Perfect Art of Canning and Preserving* (London and New York, 1891), Marion Neil's *Canning, Preserving and Pickling* (London, 1914), (Neil was a

graduate of the West End School of Cookery but wrote this book from Philadelphia), and Ola Powell's *Successful Canning and Preserving* (London and Philadelphia, 1918).

40. See for example those illustrated in O. Powell, *Successful Canning and Preserving*, pp. 10 and 51.

41. While the Banks's *Fruit and Vegetable Bottling* (1928) (see following footnote) advocates long boiling for vegetables in the preserving process, the *Radiation Cookery Book* (London, 1927) suggests the use of pressure cookers to save on heating costs.

42. W. Wilks *Fruit-Bottling* (London, 1916) was updated by V. and G. Banks in 1917, 1918, 1920 and republished as *Fruit and Vegetable Bottling, Pulping, Drying, and Canning* . . . (London, 1928). This is close to the first Ministry of Agriculture bulletin, edited by Miss M. L. Adams, *Domestic Preservation of Fruit and Vegetables*, Bulletin No. 21 (London, 1929), revised by B. A. Crang and M. Mason as *Domestic Preservation of Fruit and Vegetables* in 1942, following their *Preserves from the Garden*, also for the Ministry of Agriculture (London, 1940). The 1942 edition went through several editions to 1962.

43. The addition seems to have been reasonably common as is attested to by its presence in several recipes: for example those in *What to do with the Cold Mutton* (London, 1863); but other agents were used. A commonly used chemical was borax, for example see W. M. Williams description of the injection of boric acid into a stunned animal before it is slaughtered, in *Chemistry of Cookery* (London, 1885), pp. 170-1; and boric acid, along with benzoate of sodium and salicylic acid, were among the 'harmless preservatives' listed by O. Powell in *Canning and Preserving*.

44. Despite recognition that many chemicals are prohibited commercially after 1925, as evidenced by the comments in V. and G. Banks, *Fruit and Vegetable Bottling* (London, 1928), p. 30; but additions to domestic preserves seem to have continued. No warning against the use of campden tablets by M. Brady in *Health for All* (London, 1943), p. 98 would indicate their acceptance, substantiated by instructions for their use by the *Radiation Cookery Book* (London, 1927), by C. Grange; *The Complete Book of Home Preservation* (London, 1947) which also advocates the use of boric acid, and many other books from the 1920s to 1950s.

45. The Public Health Preservation in Food Act of August 1925 led to the January 1927 Regulation from the Ministry of Health whose list of prohibited additives resembles an early guide to E-numbers from antinomy and arsenic to zinc.

46. See D. Attar, *A Bibliography of Household Books published in England 1800-1914* (London, 1987), p. 25.

47. See for example B. F. Collier, in 'Of Ancient Recipes and old-World Cures', *The Woman's Agricultural Times*, Jan 1905, who notes that in the twentieth century there is 'the ubiquitous doctor at hand', 'every village has its store', while in the seventeenth century 'the Lady Bountiful of the country seat was also

practically the doctor for the countryside' (p. 85). Collier also explicitly compares the older family traditions of the gentlewomen, with the present need for women to combat gross manufacture with 'distinctive' taste. Also relevant are R. M. Bradley's remarks in *The English Housewife in the Seventeenth and Eighteenth Centuries* (London, 1912), where she relates the definitely 'distinctive touch' of the 'competent and intelligent housewives of the early Stuarts' to antiscientific, traditional and folkloric knowledge (p. vi).

48. V. and G. Banks, *Fruit and Vegetable Bottling*, introduction.
49. J. Bond, *A Practical Guide to the Use of Canned Foods* (London, 1938).

# Index

Acton, Eliza, 141
Adams, Fanny, 128
Adams, M. L., 151
additives, 147–8
air-drying, *see* drying
*albarellos*, 55, 57
alcohol
  as drink, 27–9
  as preservative, 91, 105–7
ale, 27–9, 60
alegar, 29, 81
almonds, 26
alum, 147
America
  health foods, 143, 146
  refrigeration, 115–16
amidon, 25–6
Ams, Charles, 128
anchovies
  mock, 70
  pickled, 70, 81
  pots, 43, 49
Andrea, Louise, 150–1
Andries, Jasper, 55
antiseptics, 105
Appert, Charles, *see* Appert,
  Nicolas
Appert, Nicolas, 93, 123–6,
  139–40
apples, 90
armies, 143
artichokes, 84, 85
ash burial, 12
atomic radiation, 129–30
Australia, 142

Back, Sir George, 110
bacon, 5, 43, 72–7
baconned herrings, 23–4
bacteria, *see* microbes
Bailey, Nathan, 71, 82–3

Banks, Sir Joseph, 123, 151
Bay salt, 20
beans
  canebens, 26
  French, 49–50
  green, 85
beef
  collaring, 80
  Martinmas beef, 71–2
  pickling, 44, 46
  potting, 87
  salting, 21, 43, 141–2
beer, *see* ale
Beeton, Mrs Isabella
  bottling, 147
  pork pickling recipe, 44–6
  salting, 143
Bell, Henry and Sir James,
  118–19
Best, Mary Ellen, 35
biltong, 9
Birdseye, Clarence, 122–3
blast freezer, 122
Blencowe, Ann, 84
bog butter, 11–12
Bond, Janet, 151
books on preservation, 134–53
bottling, 139, 146–7
  fruit, 91–4, 123, 150
  pigeons, 95
Boyle, Robert
  bottling, 92, 93
  fruit preserving, 89–90
  potting, 86
Bradley, Edith, 150
Bradley, Richard
  bacon, 71
  bottling: fruit, 92; pigeons, 95
  brawn, 79
  burial, 60
  portable soup, 84
  potting, 88

# Index

smoking, 75–6
venison pasties, 33, 34
Bradshaw, Penelope, 137
brandy, 105
brawn, 78–9, 87
bread, 25, 61–2
Brears, Peter, vi, 32–65
brining, 44, 77–8
Brown, Rose, 149
Buckland, Frank, 49
Buckland, William, 113
Buckmaster, John, 148
Buckton, Catherine, 148–9
burial
 cereals, 13–14
 dairy products, 9–13, 85
 flesh foods, 9–13
 fruits, 85, 90
 pots, 59–60
bussas, 49
butter
 bog butter, 11–12
 discovery, 18
 pots, 50–4
 potting, 88
 production, 18–19
 refrigeration, 121–2
 salting, 22–3, 68

cabbage, 85
cake soup, 84–5
Canada, 114
candy, 89
canebens, 26
Canned Foods Advisory Bureau, 151
canning, 123–9, 146, 151
*capraea*, 17
Carter, Charles, 33
Carter, Susannah, 137
catsup, 83
cereals, 25–6
 burial, 13–14: pots, 59–60
 parching, 14–15
*cervus*, 17
char, 38, 41
cheese
 making, 17–18, 22–3
 potting, 88
 smoking, 16

chemical preservation, 104–8
cherries, 95
chewetes, 36, 37
chicken, 36, 37
China
 refrigeration, 86, 114
 wind-drying, 9
cinnamon, 27
Claesz, Pieter, 36
clarified butter, 88
class and preservation, 144–5, 152
climate, influence on drying, 7, 9
Clokie's of Castleford, 40
cockscombs, 87
cod, salt, 69
coffee beans, 108–9
coffins, 36, 37
cold, *see* refrigeration
cold pies, 22
Coleman, J. J., 119
collaring, 79–80
Cook, Ann, 68, 72, 88
Cook, Captain, 84, 85
corn, *see* cereals
cornflour, 62–3
Cornish Wares, 63
Crang, 151–2
creamware pottery, 39
Crooke, May, 150
cucumbers, 83
Cullen, Dr William, 86, 116–17
curds, 17–18, 22
curing, 47, 75–6
currants, 27
Cuvier, 113

Damascus prunes, 27
damsons, 94
dates, 27
de Heine, Augustus, 126
de Swinburne, Richard, 21
Debes, Lucas, 12
deep-freezing, *see* freezing
deer, 10, 17
 *see also* venison
dehydration, 108–13
delftware pottery, 39, 41, 55–7
dessication, 108
Digby, Sir Kenelm, 37, 67

Donegal, Marquis of, 27
Donkin, Brian, 126
Donovan, Michael, 142-3
dried fruits, 27
Drummond, Sir Jack, 110
dry storage, 61-4
drying
  flesh foods, 6-9, 85
  fruits, 90
  industrially, 108-13
  stockfish, 25
duck, 9
Durand, Peter, 126, 140
Dutch beef, 71
Dwight, John, 56

earthenware, 39, 41
  bussas, 49
Edwards, 110
eggs, 58-9
Egyptians
  drying, 6
  refrigeration, 116
eisel, 29
Ekenberg, 113
Ellis, William
  bacon, 72-3, 74
  bad meat, 95
  beef, 71-2
  brawn, 79
  ham, 76
  pork, 77-8, 87
enzymes, 146-7
ether, 117-18
Evelyn, 94
export, 1

Fairclough, M., 149
famines, 1, 5
Faroe Islands
  drying, 6-8
  burial, 9, 12
fermentation, 106-7, 146
Fettiplace, Elinor, 89
fish
  burial, 9
  collaring, 80-1
  drying, 6-7
  potting, 37-8, 41-2

salting, 17, 23-5, 105
smoking, 15-16
flampoyntes, 36, 37
flies, drying process, 8-9
food poisoning, 95
formaldehyde, 16
Forsyth, Mr, 110
fowl, 86-7
Fowler, George, 146
Francatelli, Charles, 35
France
  army, 143
  fruit preserving, 90-1
  salting, 67
  wines, 28
freeze-drying, 113
freezing, 1-2, 3-4
French beans, 49-50
fruits
  bottling, 91-4, 123, 147, 150
  burial, 60, 90
  dried, 27, 90-1
  pickling, 81-3
fungi, 13

galleypots, 45
game birds, pies, 35
gannets, 85
geese, 71, 76, 85
  pies, 35, 76
Germany, 75-6
Giebert, George, 111-12
glass jars, 50, 58
Glasse, Hannah
  bad meat, 95
  beef, 80
  books, 137
  bottling, 93-4
  butter, 88
  French beans, 49-50
  gooseberries, 91-2
  hams, 67-8, 76
  lobster, 39
  mackerel, 81
  pies, 35
gluts, food, 5
Good Housekeeping Institute,
  151
goose pies, 35, 36

161

# Index

gooseberries
  bottling, 91–2
  tart, 90
Graefer, J., 110
grain, *see* cereals
gravy, potting, 88
Greek currants, 27
green bacon, 77
green beans, 85
greenfish, 23
Grigson, Jane, 143
Guy-Lussac, 140

haberden, 69
hake, 69
Halsall, A. Hill, 143
ham, 5, 17
  pickling, 46–9
  preparation, 73–7
  Westphalia, 142
Harrison, William, 78
Hartlib, 90, 93
hazel nuts, 60
health foods, 143, 146
Heine, Augustus de, 126
herbs, 28
herbal ales, 28–9
herrings, 23–4, 69–70, 105–6
hippocras, 28
Hoefnagel, 33–4, 36
Holland, 93
honey
  Egypt, 105
  in curing hams, 76
  in wines, 28–9
hops, 28
Hunter, Lynette, vi, 134–58
hydrostatic steriliser, 129, 131

ice, as preservative, *see*
    refrigeration
ice-houses, 86, 114–15
immersion bath, 121–2
import
  of food, 1, 120–1
  of ice, 142
India, 116
insects, 8–9, 10

Ireland
  bog butter, 11
  smoking, 15–16
Iron Age
  burial, 13–14
  parching, 14
  salting, 16
irradiation, 4, 130, 132
isinglass, 59
Italy, 86

jam making, 3, 89
Jansen, Jacob, 55
jellies, as preservative, 89
Just-Hatmaker, 113

Kelvin, Lord, 119
kippered herrings, 23–4
koumiss, 19

Lake, Bill, 49
lamb, 8
lamprey pies, 22, 34–5
Landt, Jorgen, 7–8
Langland, W., 22
lard pots, 53, 54
Leeuwenhoeck, 96
Leuchs, J. C., 105, 108–9
Liebig, Justus von, 110–11, 143
Lind, James, 84
Ling, 69
lobster potting, 39
Loudon, John Claudius, 115
Lounds's salt, 67

mackerel, 81
Maldon salt, 67–8
Maling, C. T., 40, 41
malnutrition, 1
mammoths, 113–14, 142
manchet, 25
mangoes, 83
Mann, E. G., 148
Markham, Gervase, 95, 137
marmalade making, 3, 89
Marquis of Donegal, 27
Martin, Martin, 7, 12–13
Martinmas beef, 71–2
Mason, 151–2

# Index

Matthew, Emily de Vere, 144
May, Robert, 79
medieval period, *see* Middle Ages
microbes
  burial, 13
  discovery, 96
  drying, 8–9, 108
  heat, 147
Middle Ages
  ale, 27–9
  cereals, 25–6
  dried fruits, 26–7
  pulses, 25–6
  salting: dairy products, 22–3;
    fish, 23–5; meat, 19–22
  spices, 26–7
  sugar, 26–7
  wine, 27–9
milk, 17, 22
Ministry of Agriculture, 151
Mohr, 125
Montagu, Duke of, 38–9
moose, 111
Moxon, Elizabeth, 59–60
Muller, H. G., vi, 104–33
mushrooms, 82, 85, 86
mustard balls, 84–5
mutton
  curing, 76
  drying, 8
  potting, 37
  salting, 21, 71
Myrdal, J., 18–19

Needham, 123
Netherlands, 93
New Zealand, 119–21, 142
nitre, 68
Norway
  fish drying, 6
  ice, 142
nuts, 60, 82, 83

oatmeal, 62–3
Oldmeadow, Ernest, 150
olive oil, 86
organic vegetables, 4
Orkney Islands, 7
oxidation, 139
oysters, 70, 81

painted pots, 55
pandemain, 25
Panton, Jane, 144
Papin digesters, 126, 129
parching, 14–15
Parmentier, Antoine, 110
Parry, Captain Sir Edward, 126–7
Pasteur, Louis, 96, 146
pasties, 33–4, 36
peas
  bottling, 125–6
  Middle Ages, 25, 26
  storage jars, 62–3
peat bogs, 11
pemmican, 110
pepper, 28
Perkins, Jacob, 117–18, 142
*perna*, 17
  *see also* ham
petre salt, 68
Pettenkover, F. X., 111
pickling
  beef, 46
  collaring, 79–81
  fruits, 81–3
  ham, 47–8
  jars, 55–8
  pork, 44–5, 77–8, 105, 107
  tongue, 46
  vegetables, 81–3
pies, 34–7, 87
pigeons, bottled, 95
pilchards, 49
piment, 28
pit storage, 14
plate freezer, 122
Platt, Sir Hugh
  hazel nuts, 60
  pickling, 79
  potting, 86–7
  venison, 95
Plot, Dr Robert, 50
plunge-churns, 19
pocket soup, 84–5
polonis, 142
Poor John, 69
pork
  chewetes, 36, 37
  flampoyntes, 36, 37
  pickled, 77–8

163

pies, 37
potting, 37–8, 87
salting, 5, 17, 71
*see also* bacon; brawn; ham
portable soup, 84–5, 110, 112
pots, 39–41
  burial, 59–60
  bussas, 49
  butter, 50–4
  dry storage, 61–4
  eggs, 58–9
  lard, 54
  pickles, 55–7
  preserves, 55–7
  salting: meat, 44–8; vegetables,
    49–50
pottages, 25–6
potteries, 39–42, 63–4
pottery industry
  decline, 43
  expansion, 32
potting
  decline, 43
  definition, 32
  introduction, 37–43
  process, 86–8
Pownall, S. Beaty, 149
preserve jars, 55–8
pressure cooking, 147
Price, Rebecca, 43–4
Proust, Joseph, 110
prunes, 27
pulses, 25–6
Pyke, Dr Magnus, 127

quick-freezing, 122
Rabisha, William, 75, 87, 88
radiation, atomic, 129–30
Raffald, Elizabeth, 137, 140
railways, influence on potteries,
    40–1
raisins, 27
recipes
  beef, pickle for, 46
  bottled pigeons, 95
  canebens, 26
  gooseberry tart, 90
  ham, pickling, 47
  pastry cases, 34

pork, pickling, 44–5
portable soup, 84
tongue, pickle for, 46
venison pasties, 33
red deer, 17
red herrings, 23–4
Redfern, F., 51
reesting, 10
refrigeration, 86, 113–23, 142
rennet, 17–18
rice, 26–7
  storage jars, 62–3
Ritchie, Professor J., 11–12
Robinson, James, 142
roe deer, 17
roller-drying, 113
rosemary, 28
Royal Horticultural Society, 147,
    150, 151
Royal Society, 92–3, 94
Rundell, Maria Eliza, 140–1, 142
Russia, 114, 142

Saddington, Thomas, 93, 123,
    139
sage wine, 28–9
salamis, 142
salmon, 70, 81
salprunella, 68
salt taxes, 69, 76
saltfish, 23
salting
  books on, 141–3
  cheese, 18
  fish, 17, 20, 23–5, 105
  flesh foods, 16–17, 20–1, 105
  pork, *see* bacon; ham
  pots for, 43–9
  process, 16–17, 20, 67–76
  vegetables, 85–6
saltpetre, 68
sauces, travelling, 84–5
sausages, 75
sauerkraut, 85
Scheele, 123
Scotland
  burial: ash, 12–13; bog butter,
    11–12
  cereals, 25

drying, 85
drying-houses, 7
refrigeration, 86
Scott, Sir Lindsay, 12–13
scurvy, 110
Senn, C. H., 145
shaking method of butter-making, 18
shrimp-paste pots, 41, 42
Skye
    bog butter, 11–12
    herring drying, 7
Smith, Eliza, 137
smoking, 15–16, 67, 74–6, 109–10
    and salting, 17, 23–4
sodium sulphite, 147
soup, 84–5, 110
sousing, 78–80
Souter, Helen, 149
Soyer, Alexis, 144
Spallanzani, 96, 123
spelt, 14
Spencer, E., 137
spices, 26, 28–9
spray-drying, 113
Spurling, Hilary, 89
St Kilda
    ash burial, 12–13
    drying, 85
    drying-houses, 7
Staffordshire potteries, 55
    butter pots, 50–2, 53
Stead, Jennifer, vi, 66–103
Steen, Jan, 35–6
steriliser, hydrostatic, 129, 131
stockfish, 25, 108
stoneware, 39–41, 49–50, 56–8, 63
Stoney, 150
storage jars, 62–4
stud holes, 128
suet, 70–1
sugar
    in books, 136, 138–40
    fruit preserving, 29, 89–90
    ham curing, 76
    import, 66, 97

jam, 105
luxury food, 26, 88–9
Swinburne, Richard de, 21
syrup, 89, 139

Taylor, D. Cottingham, 151
Tegetmeier, William, 143, 145
tin-glazing, 55
tongue, 43–4, 46
Trall, Russell, 143
transfer-printed designs, 40–2, 63
travelling sauces, 84–5
tunnel-drying, 112–13
Turner, Thomas, 91
Tusser, 70
Tyndall, 146

United States of America
    health foods, 143, 146
    refrigeration, 115–16

veal
    glue, 84–5
    hams, 76
vegetables, pickling, 81–3
vegetarianism, 146
venison
    burial, 10–11
    collaring, 87
    drying, 85
    pasties, 33, 36, 87
    salting, 17, 21
vent hole covers, 128
verjuice, 81
vinegar
    as preservative, 29, 55–6, 81–3, 136
    pots, effect on, 50
    as seasoning, 84
vitamins, 127, 146

walnuts, 82, 83
water-glass, 59
wax dipping, 90
Westphalia ham, 142
wet-curing, 47
White, Florence, 47
white herrings, 23–4
Whitson, Captain, 120

# Index

Wilks, 150
Williams, William Mattieu, 148
Williamson, Kenneth, 6–8
Wilson, C. Anne, vi-vii, 1–31
wind-drying, 9, 25
  *see also* drying
wine, 27–9
wormwood in ale, 28
Wrigley, Ammon, 60

Wüst, O., 129

X-rays, 129

yeast
  burial, 60
  drying, 85
Yorkshire Christmas pies, 35, 36
Yorkshire hams, 75